You *Are* Sensitive!

How to Survive and Thrive In a World That Doesn't Get You

Dr. Emil Faithe

Edited by Suzan Hall and Susan Faithe

ISBN 978-1-60910-571-6

Printed in the United States of America.

BookLocker.com, Inc.
2011

Disclaimer

Acknowledgement

I wish to acknowledge my wife Susan for her unending intuitive guidance, wisdom, and contributions that have helped make this book possible. Thank you, Sue, for being patient when I was not, for being supportive when others were not, and for being my angel and guide when I was lost on my path. I am humbled by your love and grateful always for our journey together.

Contents

Preface ix

Introduction 1

Part I Making Sense of Being Sensitive: An Overview 5

1. The Sensitive 7
2. All Shapes and Sizes 15
3. You Are an Empath 19
4. Food Allergies and Your Diet 29
5. Family: Who Are These Strangers? 41
6. Being Invisible 53
7. Healthcare for the Sensitive 61
8. Poverty Pledge 79
9. The Intuitive Sensitive 88
10. Hibernation Override Syndrome 93
11. Why Am I Here, Really? 100
12. Lost My Mind, Came to My Senses 114

Part II The Sensitive's Solutions to Daily Challenges 121

How to Manage

Mood Swings 123
Colds and Flu 126
Food Cravings and Hypoglycemia 129
Anxiety and Panic 131
Hormonal Imbalances and Fibroid Cysts 134
Candida Infections 138
Foggy Headedness 141
Chronic Fatigue 143
Gas and Constipation 146
Stress Headaches 149
Low Thyroid Function 152
Asthma 154

Gallbladder Problems....157
Insomnia....160
Anemia....163
Weight Issues....166
Oral Hygiene....170
Porous Bones....172
Environmental Toxicity....175
The Aging Process....178
Pent-up Anger....181
Bug Bites....184
The Jewelry Paradox....187
Spirit Attachments....190

How to

Survive Getting Out of Bed Each Morning....193
Cope with a Nine-to-Five Job....195
Enjoy Sensitive Sex....197
Avoid Suicide....200
Communicate with Your Guides....203
Experience Joy in Your Life....206

About the Author....209

Preface

In life, sometimes it takes a while for things to make sense. Sometimes it hits you right away. I knew early on in my life that I wasn't like everybody else. I also realized as early as I can remember that I had a hard time relating to others. I didn't get them, and they didn't get me. Oh, don't get me wrong. I could feel their pain and I could sense their angst, and pretty much everything else. I just didn't know at the time what it was. I thought it was just me. Yep, I thought that what I was feeling was normal for an eight-year-old kid growing up in Southern California.

Was there something wrong with me? Had I landed on the wrong planet? Well, I couldn't be certain about the last one, and, to tell you the truth, I'm still not sure. But I was sure about one thing. I was sensitive. Sensitive to so many things--to everything, really. I just didn't realize what that meant yet. My mood, my energy, my passion for living, all seemed to be so easily squelched by people's negative energies and negative moods, by angered words, feuding parents, mean siblings, changes in the weather, job expectations, and especially the foods I ate. Everything around me seemed to affect my life, and not in a good way.

Almost fifty years later, I finally have a clear picture of what was really going on back then. More important, I now realize that I was not alone. There were and still are others, millions of others, who suffer from the same maladies, the same symptoms that I did. Many of them have told me about their long-standing feelings of loneliness, sadness, confusion, and unease at being tossed into this energetically convoluted world.

Many of these ultra-sensitive people have been drawn to my healing practice. In my office I have seen them crying, lost, confused, filled with anxiety and sadness, troubled by life-long mood issues. Many have been saddled with failures in all avenues of existence--broken relationships, workplace problems, and financial woes. Most of these people have had no clue why all this was happening to them.

Yes, I began to learn that there was a whole sub-population of us out there that was going through our own "sensitive hell." As I began to pay closer attention I began to realize that these people came from everywhere, from all walks of life, and now they had become a part of mine; a part that I could no longer ignore.

Early in 2009, the whole scenario struck me like a ton of bricks. The unrecognized masses of ultra-sensitives needed guidance and a guide, a place to learn not just how to survive, but how to thrive on the journey down their life path. Sure, there were a precious few books out there about people who are sensitive, but none that addressed the core issues of survival, and none that offered a direct, practical approach to living the sensitive life.

The plight of the ultra-sensitive certainly caught my attention, and I was intent on doing something about it. I wanted to write this book. I needed to put off the project for a while due to other commitments, but the universe would have none of that. In late 2009, I felt compelled to pick up the pieces and pull them together to bring this material to life.

It is with heartfelt intent and pleasure that I present this material to you, to those who have been seeking and not finding, to all of those who have dedicated their existence to a higher cause.

From the universe to you,

Emil Israel Faithe
Albuquerque, New Mexico

Introduction

Pssst…There's something you need to know. Something likely no one else will tell you. YOU are sensitive. Not just "a little" sensitive. *Ultra-sensitive!*

Ultra-sensitive. What exactly does that mean? It means you're different than many of the others in your life. Different than your friends, different than your co-workers, even different than your siblings or other close family members.

For those who need a simple, concise explanation, let me provide you with the one that I give to the ultra-sensitives in my private practice: "You are wired differently than everyone else." It's a good thing.

YOU ARE AN ULTRA-SENSITIVE!

Not by accident, the term ultra-sensitive not only implies that you are more sensitive than others, but that you are also part of an important, largely overlooked and, as yet, unrecognized subset of the population on this planet. Ultra-sensitives like you and I, and so many others make up this fascinating and gifted group of individuals.

As an ultra-sensitive you are an extreme empath. That means you feel EVERYTHING. You feel the energies of people, the planet, and everything on it. You feel and sense everything, even if you don't do so consciously.

So what's so special about being an ultra-sensitive? Everything. Ultra-sensitives feel things others do not. Ultra-sensitives sense things others do not. Ultra-sensitives see things others do not. As you will discover, if you haven't already, ultra-sensitives perceive and respond to the events and inhabitants of this planet in ways others do not. Ultra-sensitives view and experience their time on Earth in a whole different way than others do. That's not a bad thing, but it can leave the naïve and uninformed ultra-sensitive with a whole lot of questions. Got your list?

YOU'RE NOT ALONE

Until now, most ultra-sensitives have had no idea what makes them different, only that they know they are. Throughout my early life as an ultra-sensitive I had nowhere to turn for answers. I felt completely alone and isolated, on my own little island.

So many other ultra-sensitives I encountered had similar complaints. They had nowhere to turn and no one to turn to, to gain a better understanding of exactly what *was* different about them. They didn't dare approach friends or family, for fear they would be looked at as though… they were wearing a halo. (Perhaps they were.) There was nowhere for them to turn, until now.

Many ultra-sensitives have wanted to ask, and fewer have been able to answer: "*Why* do I feel different than the others? And since I am different, how do I make the most of my lifetime?" And, of course, they ask themselves that universal question for which everyone is seeking an answer, if not consciously then most certainly at the soul level: "What am I really here to do in this life?"

Throughout history, ultra-sensitives have had to live with these questions unanswered. Many have managed in silence, many suffering emotional and physical pain, many feeling lost and alone, for a lifetime, for millennia. No more.

It's time to be recognized. It's time to be acknowledged.
It's time for answers.

The chapters that follow have been created and arranged to help you find the answers to these questions, and much more. They have been designed to activate you, so that you will gain the deep insight you have been longing for, learn about the *you* you never knew, and to gain a better understanding about your existence on this planet, and perhaps others.

More important, this work has been brought forth to help you achieve the joy, satisfaction, and recognition that you so greatly deserve as an ultra-sensitive.

Many would argue that this recognition and activation is long overdue. I would argue that the timing is perfect, as always. As I write these words you are changing, the planet is changing, the people around you are changing, *and the Universe is changing*, in ways never before seen.

This world and others are in great need, dire need, of what you came here to do as an ultra-sensitive, and who you came here to become.

This is the time to become. As one ultra-sensitive to another, I welcome you to your new world.

Part I

Making Sense of Being Sensitive: An Overview

1.

The Sensitive

Babies all seem to look pretty much the same when they're first born. Yes, we look pretty darn similar during our first few days and weeks of life, often wearing that same goofy baby cap the hospital staff slips on for that newborn photo. We're all cute and cuddly, and everyone loves us. But make no mistake. On the inside, we are far from being the same.

Oh, sure, we all have the same basic needs after our escape from the womb; food, water, and lots of love and nurturing. But soon after birth our physical appearance starts to change. We develop our own unique identity, and our unique energy imprint. We begin to develop our own distinct emotional states and our own feelings and sensations, and those are most certainly as varied as the colors of the rainbow.

With that we begin to perceive the world, and those in it, in our own unique way, processing the information and energies of the Planet, based on our unique, genetically coded DNA strands. True, we may all be from the same species, but our paths of development can be quite different, and from one another's perspectives, even unexplainable.

POPULATION: YOU, ELEVATION: HIGH

Among the various paths of development, there exists on this planet a subgroup of beings with exquisite sensitivities to the energies of people, electronics, and other objects, animate as well as inanimate. And these beings come from all walks of life and from all cultures. It matters not where you hail from--Lodz, Poland; Sydney, Australia; Essex, Connecticut; or an island in the Bahamas. This special, long-overlooked subgroup of the population is made up of people from all across the globe.

Yes, there are those of us out there, from the far corners of this planet, perhaps others, that are part of an as of yet unidentified and unrecognized subgroup of Earth's population… the ULTRA-SENSITIVE. *You* are one of those people.

FEEL THIS

Now, for some of you this realization is nothing new. You've known that you were different from the rest of the population all along. It's your little secret from the rest of the world. Yet for many others who are now just awakening and experiencing these unexplainable "feelings" for the first time, this news may come as quite a surprise, and perhaps even a relief.

So what exactly *are* you feeling? Everything. You feel everything, in ways others do not. Your receiver, your processor is exquisitely sensitive, different from the others. That is to say, the way you receive and perceive yourself and your surroundings is much more amplified than the norm, and these energy signals have a much more profound impact on your being than those who are less sensitive.

SENSITIVE YOU

Sensitive? Yes, *you*. You are sensitive. Has anybody ever told you that? Well, maybe it's about time somebody did.

So, what does that mean, exactly--sensitive?

Does that mean that you cry at the drop of a hat? Does that mean that you can't eat certain foods without feeling lousy? Perhaps it's because you react differently to certain sounds or colors. Maybe you just understand people, places, and things in ways others don't. Or maybe you just feel things, or sense things, or know things as no else does. Is that what being sensitive is all about? Yes. It's all that, and much more.

Sure, everyone on this planet is sensitive to some degree, even the professional wrestler, the thief, the politician that makes you crazy, even the grumpy grandma, the burley ball player, the ballerina, or the psychic. We're all equipped with the ability and the internal equipment to be sensitive. That's a major aspect of our "humanness." But as with many other attributes we may be born with, like the gift of gab, the gift of writing, the ability to play great football, some people are more gifted than others. In this case, you are more sensitive than most other people. That's right. Your gift is your sensitivity.

HOW SENSITIVE ARE YOU?

Not sure how sensitive you really are? Let's find out.

Take the sensitivity test:

1. Do fragrances and other chemicals give you headaches or muscle aches?
2. Does going grocery shopping, or being out in public feel almost as painful as a root canal?
3. Are you often bullied by friends, neighbors, family members, or workmates?
4. Does sitting under fluorescent lights or in front of a computer screen exhaust you to the extent that bedtime can't come soon enough?
5. Does your mood often feel like *Mr. Toad's Wild Ride*?
6. Does eating cheese, wheat, strawberries, tomatoes, or other foods easily bring on skin rashes, itching, or digestive symptoms that defy logic?
7. Do you feel anxious and uncomfortable in situations that should give you pleasure, such as dining out, going to the movies, or other social events?
8. Do you have an intense appreciation of the arts, music, and nature?
9. Do you ever go into a room filled with certain people and come out feeling nauseous, anxious, fatigued, depressed, or just plain uncomfortable?
10. Are you often ignored or overlooked in social and work conversations or events?
11. When you hear about or see people that are suffering, do you feel like crying, or taking on their pain?
12. Are you easily moved by emotional scenes in books, movies, or plays?
13. Does entering an old building, or a room filled with old books or other objects make you feel anxious or sad?

14. Do you feel, hear, or see things that others don't?
15. Do you often wonder why you're here on Planet Earth?

SENSITIVITY METER

How many of the above situations can *you* identify with?

Less than 5 – Your sensitivity is under construction; things are stirring within you.

5 to 10 – You are sensitive. You are in the throes of ultra-sensitive development; uncertain as to what's happening to you, but certain something is.

10 to 15 – Congratulations! You are a full-fledged ultra-sensitive! You are ready and able to make a significant contribution to this planet and those who inhabit it. Your time is now.

If you've known all along that you were sensitive, that you were different from the others, and you scored less than ten matches, don't worry. You are most definitely sensitive. That's why you picked up this book; to find out more about what being "sensitive" really means; to learn how to make the most of this lifetime as an ultra-sensitive; and finally, how to deal with the unique life situations that face ultra-sensitives everywhere.

Whether you scored one match or all fifteen, all is perfect. You are about to uncover a whole new aspect of yourself; an aspect that will likely change the way you see yourself, the way you see others, and the way you see the world you live in.

Are you ready for the ultra-sensitive journey?

IT'S NOT A ROSE GARDEN

Being sensitive is a gift. This gift gives us the capacity to make perfect decisions about our life. It provides us with the tools to help and guide us and others, in our health and in life. It gives us the ability to explore aspects of life we'd never learn in any school. It's a vast storehouse of unlimited potential just waiting to put to good use.

However, most ultra-sensitives would tell you that these gifts, these skills and the gain they can achieve often come at a hefty price--what some might perceive as a personal sacrifice. Yes, for some, living the life of an ultra-sensitive may indeed seem like a sacrifice; a sacrifice that can make even the most devoted and steadfast feel as though they have been ridiculed, misunderstood, and forsaken.

I would suggest that rather than perceiving your life as a "sacrifice" it might better be considered a gift--a gift from you to everyone else around you. It's the mark you leave during this lifetime, an aspect of yourself that you came here to gift to others. In other words, it's part of what we came here to do. But do be clear. The process of imparting this gift, of leaving your mark, may not always feel like a rose garden.

DOES ANYBODY REALLY UNDERSTAND ME?

Being an ultra-sensitive is not always an easy or pleasant undertaking. As you will see as you navigate through this material, being a sensitive person on Planet Earth can be challenging, draining, and rewarding all at once; it's an experience and adventure that you won't soon forget. (And we never do.) But be reassured that you're not alone on your journey, and there are many others out there who *do* understand who you are and what you're going through. How do I know this? I'm one of those people. I do understand. And that's why I brought this material to life.

STEP INTO MY OFFICE

Over the years, many people from all walks of life have shared their stories in my office, most complaining about physical and emotional symptoms that literally defy logic. And they all had the same MO: crying, depressed, unhappy, lost…exhausted. Their hormones grossly out of balance. Their adrenal glands drained. Most were insomniacs, fatigued, and constantly dealing with weight and nutrition problems, underweight or overweight.

Until they ended up in my office, most of these ultra-sensitives had no idea what was wrong with them. They believed that there was something seriously physically awry. Many had spent time in emergency rooms, psychiatrist's offices, or, worse yet, been exposed to numerous "medical tests" and harsh prescription pills, before we visited.

Thousands of dollars and months or years later, they were no better, and in many cases, worse. The mainstream medical community had little or no explanation for their symptoms and instead attached labels and stigmas to these vulnerable ultra-sensitives. Without conclusive physical findings and test results and for lack of diagnostic terminology, ultra-sensitives began to acquire labels: Chronic Fatigue Syndrome, Fibromyalgia, ADHD, Bipolar Disorder, Lupus, Depression, Social Phobia and more.

Yes, the traditional healthcare system has its own theory. If you are a physically healthy ultra-sensitive with these types of symptoms, it must all be in your head. Sorry. That's just not the case.

The happy truth is that most of these ultra-sensitive people really do have nothing medically wrong with them. They are simply experiencing the predictable effects of their ultra sensitivity, which, in my experience, are completely correctable.

WHAT WAS I THINKING?

The very next question the astute ultra-sensitive asks is: "Why would I ask to have a life of misery?"

I've got to tell you, that is the question I have been asking myself for the fifty plus years I've been on the planet. Why is everything so difficult? Why does everything seem like such a challenge? And I mean everything from A to Z. From picking out a birthday card, to renting a house, to finding foods I can tolerate, to getting through the workday, to healing the planet. And even with the struggles, why does it seem that success in every area of my life is so elusive?

WHY ME?

Most ultra-sensitives that I've had the privilege of working with either ask this question or want to. Why is this happening to me? Why am I so sensitive? Many go on to speculate: Am I being punished for something I did in a past life? Is my life cursed? Why am I broke? Why am I depressed? Why am I exhausted? Why me? These are the battle cries of the ultra-sensitives.

The answers aren't always easy to swallow. And as an ultra-sensitive club member it wasn't easy for me either. Believe it or not:

- We agreed to live this life, this way, prior to coming into body. We made this contract.
- We chose to experience as much soul evolution as possible in the shortest period of time possible.
- We came here to assist ourselves and others during the transition into the "Golden Age."

And not just during any time in history. This era you and I were born into isn't just any old era. We contracted to come into this life matrix during the most powerful, intense, and profound energy shifts ever witnessed, on this planet or beyond. And we demanded a front row seat, with popcorn, for the biggest show on Earth. And guess what? That's exactly what they gave us.

JUST BE THERE

It is no coincidence (and really, there are no coincidences) that we are all here on the same cruise-ship, voyaging together during these monumental times. Indeed, we all agreed to be here at the same time, these times, to work together to achieve this soul evolution, each in our own unique way.

Yet, many ultra-sensitives would argue that they have failed miserably at this task. Nothing could be farther from the truth. Despite what we might perceive about our success with regard to the size of our bank accounts, or the number of expensive cars and influential friends we have, as ultra-sensitives we have succeeded, and continue to succeed, beyond our wildest wishes. What we are accomplishing, even as you read this material, is truly beyond our conscious comprehension.

If you could only see how much you have brought, and continue to bring, to this planet and its inhabitants, how much light and healing you bring to so many, just by your existence here. It's true. Many of you are capable of healing and balancing the energies of the planet and its occupants simply by being around them.

Has this ever happened to you; have you ever spent time hanging around with someone, a friend, an acquaintance, and then have them tell you how much better they feel? They can't explain why they feel better. They just do. There you were, doing what you came here to do, without you even knowing it. That's how it works. We are, and therefore we heal, others and even ourselves, without even lifting a finger.

You just changed someone's life forever,
and you didn't even know it.

As you can see, it's not necessarily a big financial windfall or an earth shaking outcome we came here to manifest. It's the monumental little things. More times than not, the little things we do each day have the largest impact on the many others.

So, from now on, begin to pay attention to all the little things you do every single day. When you do, you'll begin to see, or at least get a small taste of, what you came here to do. And then you'll realize that indeed, YOU are doing it.

Why did you choose to be an ultra-sensitive? Ah, now you remember!

Yes, this is a magical time to be alive. This is a magical time to be an ultra-sensitive. So you ask, why me? Why an ultra-sensitive? Now you know. You have been blessed with this opportunity.

2.

All Shapes and Sizes

People come in many shapes and styles, from the very petite to the extra large, from the meek to the macho. Like you, I've met all varieties. One thing I've learned is that outward appearance has absolutely nothing to do with what's inside. A sensitive is a sensitive, no matter what color, shape, size, or sexual orientation. Yes, that worn out cliché still holds true. Don't judge a book by its cover.

HOW CAN YOU TELL?

That's the most common response when I inform people that they are an ultra-sensitive, even if it's just a causal encounter at the grocery store. The answer? I sense their aura, their energy field. I see and feel their powers, and their gifts. As a sensitive and intuitive, it's difficult for me to ignore the energies of others, especially ultra-sensitives. I know that I've encountered one when I feel as if I've been blinded by a beacon of light. Because in truth I have. And so have you from time to time. You just didn't realize what you were feeling, until now.

Sure, I do my best to keep my radar off when I'm relaxing and away from the office, but sometimes these interactions are unavoidable. That's because ultra-sensitives are everywhere, in the most unexpected locations and situations, playing out the most unexpected roles.

THE SOFT SIDE OF SENSITIVES

Many gifted ultra-sensitives go about their rough and tumble lifestyles, their dead end jobs, or their lackluster home lives, never suspecting that deep down inside a volcano is brewing, with molten emotions, sensations, and more, bubbling to the surface. In fact, as you read these words, ultra-sensitives around the globe are beginning to awaken to these monumental changes occurring within them. They are in the process of self-activation, activation into the ultra-sensitives they are, and it's a beautiful thing. Many of these people may not look the part of an ultra-sensitive. But it doesn't matter. Their softer side is rising to the top.

Most ultra-sensitives will admit that they knew they were different, but they just didn't know in what way. And simply because of their looks, or their station in life, no one else around them had a clue, either. The packaging didn't disclose the content. I had one of those encounters one day long ago, and it changed my life.

ESTEVAN

Estevan was a large Hispanic man, with a tall build and a macho look. He worked in a busy pharmacy, with irate customers and expensive pills. His job was to deal with some of the most cumbersome left-brain computer glitches around, and he did it well. He was a great employee, hard working, dedicated, and quiet. It seemed that Estevan was indeed entrenched in the rote world of a nine-to-five job; a job that dealt with the unemotional and less-sensitive aspects of our society. Yet it was a job that needed to be done.

When I first worked with Estevan he struck me as the last person on the planet who would understand the meaning of intuition, planetary shifts, or past life regressions. He looked like a retired football player, and he was a man of very few words. Oh, sure, we conversed now and again, but always about business.

This particular day and time we'd hit a lull in the activity. Then out of nowhere came the question. He turned to me with a serious look on his face, and when he asked it, he answered all of mine: "Hey, Emil. Do you ever feel like there's more to life than we really see?"

My jaw dropped. I took a moment to think about how I wanted to respond. After all, we both worked for a straight-laced corporate conglomerate. What would people think if they found out that one of

> their highly paid, white collar professionals was into spooks and intuition, and everything holistic? Did I want all of my co-workers, bosses, and the world to know that I'm not who I seem? Was it safe? Maybe I'd be ridiculed or, worse yet, possibly fired. In that one moment, all those thoughts bounced around in my head.
>
> And what of Estevan? Wasn't he afraid of being "found out?" Apparently not.
>
> It was right there and then that I realized it was not just mandatory, but physically and emotionally necessary for me to be true to myself: to who I am and to what I do. I could no longer worry about what others would think of me. It didn't matter anymore. Estevan felt the same way. It was quite an ice breaker. Here was an ultra-sensitive in disguise, eager to connect with someone like-minded.
>
> Once we broke the ice, Estevan couldn't get enough. We talked. We talked about all things sensitive: intuition, planetary shifts, UFO's, ghosts and, of course, holistic healing. Not only was he interested, it turned out that his entire off-time was consumed with exploring of these subjects and more.
>
> We forged a new relationship that day. We took a risk that others might learn about our secret gifts, our intuition, our real world as ultra-sensitives. And I've got to tell you, it felt great to be out of the closet.
>
> Until that day, I had believed that I could identify an ultra-sensitive whenever I ran into one. This one caught me by surprise, and it changed my whole perspective on how *not* to judge a book by its cover. It also instilled new hope that we are out there, all over. We were not alone. It was a great day.

I don't care how loud and deep your voice is. It doesn't matter if you're seven-feet tall and play basketball for the Lakers. It doesn't matter if you drive a dump truck, haul rubbish for a living, or knit scarves for the elderly. It doesn't matter if you work for the FBI, CIA, the U.S. Navy or Baskin Robbins. Whatever you do, wherever you are, you will always be who you are on the inside, the softer side that no one else can see…yet.

WHAT'S YOUR GIG?

Are you the research scientist turned healer? Are you the schoolteacher turned spiritual leader? Maybe you're the nurse or doctor turned energy worker. It matters not. What does matter is that you've come here not just to work for a paycheck, but to make a difference in ways you never consciously dreamed possible. And the time is now. And the place is Planet Earth. Are you ready?

COME OUT OF THE CLOSET

It's that time on the planet where all ultra-sensitives are scheduled to become activated, no matter where you are, or what you look like, or your current station in life. So don't allow the judgment or the leering looks of others keep you from becoming everything you came here to be. Their comprehension of who you really are may not fit into their narrow scope of what's going on the planet, but that's their lesson, not yours. More important, don't judge *yourself* by what you see in the mirror, or by what you think others see in your mirror. Just be yourself. All of yourself. Always.

From now on, honor those twinges of intuition you are beginning to experience, experiment with the gifts of healing that are just waiting for your attention. Honor all of the gifts that are tucked inside you, the one's you've been holding onto all of your life. Then live--really live the life of the ultra-sensitive you are. Don't wait. We need you now!

Oh, and by the way. You don't need to submit a picture with your application for the position of ultra-sensitive, unless it's a Kirlian photo of your aura.

3.

You Are an Empath

Perhaps you've already figured this one out. Ultra-sensitives are sensitive to everything. Very sensitive. That's because you are an empath. You feel everything. You feel energies. Not just some types of energies but all types of energies, including the energies of people. Why? Because everything, including you and me, is nothing but energy. And any time we interact with *any* energy source it can affect our own, unless we learn how to protect ourselves. Not with weapons, fences or doors, but by protecting our personal energy space, our aura.

THE AURA

Each of us has an aura, our personal energy field that contains our unique energy imprint. Suffice it to say, the aura is an energy buffer between the outside and your *inside* world. As such, anything that intersects your aura can directly affect your energy field and profoundly affect the way you feel physically and emotionally. A positive energy exposure can make you feel energized, motivated, and elated. However, a negative energy exposure can quickly ruin your day, as you'll soon see.

WHAT'S IN YOUR AURA?

As ultra-sensitives we go about our daily activities and our lives accumulating unwanted energies from everyone and everything we come in contact with, mostly without our approval or our knowledge. Think about the number of people, places, and things you interact with in just a single day. Then multiply that multi-fold and you can get a sense of the type of energy load ultra-sensitives are exposed to over a lifetime. That's quite an exposure.

Over time, these accumulations of energies which are not of our own making can easily overwhelm the vulnerable ultra-sensitive, making us feel nothing short of horrible. Many of these negative energy exposures occur from our exposure to electronics, that is, electromagnetic fields (EMF's), which can come from a number of sources.

Do you feel out of sorts on a regular basis? Here are just a few examples of "things" that emit EMF energies that can easily disrupt your sensitive aura:

Electromagnetic field emitters:

- Cell phones (even if they're off)
- Computers (even if they're off)
- Televisions and radios (even if they're off)
- iPods (even if they're off)
- Ley lines
- Microwave towers
- Microwave ovens
- Wind and other weather changes
- Spirit attachments
- Fluorescent lights
- Burial grounds or historic sites
- Mountain formations
- Vortexes (Earth energy centers)
- People

People?...Yes, people.

NICE TO MEET YOU?

As an ultra-sensitive, you are extra susceptible to taking on the energies of other people. That's because energy is contagious. Think of energies as you would fleas. They can easily hop from one person to another, even from a distance. Need proof? Hang around angry and depressed people, and you'll eventually begin to feel angry and depressed. Hang around happy, upbeat people; you will soon begin to feel happy and upbeat. That's how it works. It's not magic. It's nature at work.

Unfortunately, so many ultra-sensitives run through their entire lives not realizing that many of the symptoms they are experiencing *are not even their own*! We're often experiencing the energies, and symptoms, that came from someone else, and often from more than one person. That's right. In many cases, the energies belong to people we've never even met. We've picked up these energies through casual encounters in the grocery store, the bowling alley, the mall, a concert, or in our own homes...*anywhere.* The lesson: Choose your company wisely, and outfit your aura with an etheric flea collar.

If you want to stay healthy and vital as an ultra-sensitive on this planet, it's imperative that you learn to keep your aura clear of unwanted energies and attachments, lest you manifest unwanted symptoms.

In fact, ultra-sensitives who fail to clear and keep clear their personal energy fields can develop literally any physical or emotional symptom imaginable, potentially throwing them into the convoluted traditional health care system. And you don't want to end up there. If you do, the underlying cause of your symptoms (namely, negative energy exposures) will likely never be uncovered, and worse yet, you may become another unwilling guinea pig.

Symptoms of negative auric field exposures:

- Depression
- Confusion
- Inability to focus
- Panic and anxiety
- Insomnia
- Paranoia
- Hypertension
- Muscle and joint pain
- Bipolar symptoms
- Unwanted thoughts
- Chronic Fatigue Syndrome and other immune disorders
- Dizziness
- Headaches

YOU ARE AN EMPATH

All ultra-sensitives are empaths. We are sensitive receivers of energies and emotions (which are just energy). We feel everyone else's pain, anxiety, sadness...you name it. It's who we are. It's what we do. And it's the hallmark of an ultra-sensitive. The gift of *feeling.*

As such, we need to pay very close attention to energies that don't feel right. You need to practice careful discernment every day, around everybody, and everywhere you go. If you have a private practice as an intuitive, healer, or energy worker, this type of discernment is not only smart, it's crucial to maintaining your health, vitality, and longevity. Unfortunately, many ultra-sensitive practitioners fail to trust their gift of discernment. If you fail to do so, over time you will likely become ill.

STELLA

Stella was a thirty-three-year-old classic ultra-sensitive. She was a gifted healer that found herself in a quandary. She had become so sick and debilitated she could no longer work on her patients. She contacted me from across the globe after scouring the Internet for help.

Stella was very sick, even by my standards. She had gotten to the point that she couldn't eat most foods without developing a massive immune response, one that consisted of muscle aches, diarrhea, headaches, and severe depression and anxiety. Her energy was so weak she could barely speak.

I listened to her describe her long, unhealthy plight as an ultra-sensitive: her failed relationships, her exquisite sensitivities to foods and energies, and her household and lifestyle troubles. She went on to tell me that she had been to a number of renowned shamans and healers throughout the country. Yet none were able to bring her back to the land of the living. She told me that she was about to give up and go die, and that I was her last hope.

Now that last cry for help may seem like some kind of ego trip opportunity to some practitioners. Well, it was quite the opposite for me. Yes, I have seen and continue to see some of the most mysterious and complicated cases on the planet, but I wasn't sure I even wanted to take this one on. Frankly, I wasn't sure there was still time to save her.

After much soul searching and a little nudge from her guides and mine, I agreed to take the case, but only if she followed my plan exactly as I laid it out. Stella agreed.

I performed my usual top-to-bottom evaluation. I explored her diet, organ function, environment, energy field, everything.

It didn't take long to uncover her first major problem. Stella was severely undernourished due to mal-absorption of foods, combined with her unwillingness to eat them. We needed to work quickly. I started her on a potent digestive enzyme, probiotics, several antiviral and liver cleansing supplements, and more.

Within five days of starting the regimen, Stella actually had some spark back in her voice. She was astounded at how well she felt, and how she could suddenly tolerate the foods I prescribed for her. I had wanted to wait until her life force was restored, and now was the time to drop the bombshell.

I informed Stella that the underlying cause of all of her symptoms was that her auric field was congested with hundreds of entities, disembodied spirits that she had picked up during her work as a healer. To my surprise, she wasn't a bit surprised. She went on to confess that she had recently moved to a town that was well known to house industries that emitted electrical *and nuclear energy*. See, Stella was a healer, an empath, an ultra-sensitive, and she quickly and easily picked up all of these energies, without realizing it.

The combination of disembodied energies and the heavy metal emissions, namely plutonium, were enough to send her body and mind into a devastating downward spiral. Fortunately, we caught her just before she hit ground zero.

I asked my wife, Susan, a gifted energy worker, to perform an emergency session with Stella, to clear her aura of these energies and entities. And she did. Stella did remain faithful to the regimen I set for her, including a heavy metal detoxification program.

Within three weeks of our initial conversation, Stella had come back to life. She was energetic, motivated, full of spunk. So much so that she asked if she could resume her healing practice, immediately. I asked her to wait several weeks before attempting her healing work on others, and made sure she understood who she was and how sensitive she was.

A month later she did resume her practice, but not before we had a strong discussion about how to protect herself from everything that could impact her aura, especially electronics and spirit attachments. She followed my advice. She kept dark stones on her person and around her office, and took the salt and soda baths nightly as I recommended.

Today, Stella continues her work as a healer, and works equally hard to keep her body and auric field clear of energetic clutter every day.

CLEAN IT UP

Your aura, that is. Because of our ultra sensitivity to everything, ultra-sensitives must consciously "clean" their auras on a regular basis. Failure to do so could leave you with the "Stella Syndrome." And you don't want that. It you're an ultra-sensitive, and especially if you're an ultra-sensitive practitioner, cleanse your aura daily, and after each patient or client.

How to cleanse your aura:

Perform this bedtime ritual at least several times a week, or even nightly, if you feel you've been "contaminated."

- Add 1/4 cup each of baking soda and non-iodized salt to comfortable bath water.

- Make sure you cover all parts of your body with the solution (don't get the water in your eyes, nose, or mouth).
- Soak for about twenty minutes.
- Now, sleep well!

KEEP IT CLEAN

Salt and soda baths are one good way to keep your aura clean. Another way is to avoid all exposures to people, places and things. Right. Unfortunately, this method is just unrealistic for most of us. That's because we still have to interact with the world outside our front door in order to survive and thrive. Here's another option:

When you can't avoid the exposure to people, places, and things, protect yourself by keeping dark stones on your person and in your office. Dark stones will absorb the energies emitted from these sources, so that you and your aura do not.

Which stones work best to absorb these types of energy exposures? Black tourmaline, black onyx, and hematite are three good choices. Pick one or all three in sizes and shapes that work for you, and keep them on you, in your pocket, purse, or briefcase as you move through your day. It's very important, however, that you clear these stones each night, before you use them again. This can be accomplished by running water over them, or by setting them on a window-sill so that the moonlight can clear them. In the morning, they will be fresh and ready to protect you once again. (See Part II: *How to Manage Spirit Attachments*)

You can also use specimen-size stones to deflect and absorb EMF from electrical devices. I keep a specimen size piece of black tourmaline, about eight pounds, sitting right in front of my computer monitor. If I did not, I wouldn't be able to spend more than twenty minutes at a time in front of the monitor without feeling exhausted. Then it would have taken perhaps ten years to finish this book. And this material couldn't wait that long.

You may also purchase EMF deflectors that are designed to fit on your cell phone, cordless phone, television, radio, iPod, game box and more, even your computer monitor and PCU. These devices can absorb the EMF's so that they don't interfere with your aura and your immune system, and so that they don't disable your own radar system. The devices retail for about $20 each and I encourage you to consider them, because they work, and because you're worth every penny. Use them faithfully to improve your health and longevity.

So now that you've cleared your aura and protected your aura, now let's take a closer look at how to control your aura so that you can avoid all that negativity out there.

FAR OUT

As we've seen, the aura is our personal energy signature, and a dynamic and sensitive receiver of energies. It's also a very dynamic field. Its shape and size can change from moment to moment.

When you're feeling lax and open, your aura can expand dozens of feet, even hundreds of feet, away from the body, making your energy imprint more detectable by others. Now that may sound like a good thing. But having your aura unconsciously or carelessly open and vulnerable in the company of others can also be a detriment to your health and wellbeing. If you wish to protect yourself from the energies of others you need to learn how to consciously open and close your aura, at will.

CONTROL YOUR AURA

You can, you know. Just start paying attention to your surroundings. Start paying attention to how you're feeling when you're in certain places and situations, or around certain people. If you get into a situation where something or someone doesn't feel right, protect yourself and conserve your precious sensitive energy. Learn to consciously pull your aura back close to your body, to make it fit around you like a glove. Just imagine an accordion moving back in and out. You can do this. Let's practice.

Try this simple exercise:

I recommend you perform this exercise in the privacy of your personal sanctuary, wherever that is. Once you learn good aura control, you can then safely practice these skills in the outside world.

Start by protecting yourself. Place a purple transmuting light, or whichever color light you wish, around yourself. I also recommend that you keep your dark stones around you while you perform this exercise. Now we're ready to begin.

- Close your eyes and take several cleansing breaths
- Take a few moments to tune in to your aura. Take your time...That's it. Feel that energy. It's all around you. When you locate the energy you'll feel a comforting, nurturing sensation. That's because that energy is you.
- Now, take a few moments to consciously pull your aura close to your body. Imagine it fitting like a glove over your physical shape. Good. Now take several moments to sense how that feels. You should feel very safe and protected.
- Hold your aura in place for a few seconds, or a few minutes, until you're ready to release it once again.
- Now, release your aura and push it out well beyond your body. Take your time with this. Start by envisioning it expanding and filling the room, then the entire building. Take a moment to sense how that feels.
- When you're ready, practice pushing your aura further and further out. If it feels safe, push your aura around the world, by envisioning places like China, Greece, or wherever you choose to send your energy. Take a moment to sense how that feels.

At first, moving your aura away from your body may make you feel vulnerable or uncomfortable in other ways. Once you master control of your aura, these feelings of uneasiness should subside.

Continue to practice this aura exercise until you feel comfortable with your control. Then when you're ready, the next time you are out in public, or in a space around people that you wish to be protected from, practice your control again, and again. Soon you will become a master of aura control, and of your own personal energy domain.

SEE ME, FEEL ME

On the other hand, there may be times when you wish to be "recognized." You may be at a meeting, an event, or a party where you wish to engage the energies of others. If so, allow your aura to fill that space, and then, enjoy! You're bound to make the connection. After a very short while, controlling your aura will become as natural as opening and closing your eyes, or as playing the accordion, if you are so inclined.

Some ultra-sensitives have already mastered aura control. If you are an ultra-sensitive healer, intuitive, or energy worker, I urge you to master these techniques for your own safety and wellbeing. Use them in addition to your other protection techniques.

The aura is a magical, powerful, and important tool for the ultra-sensitive. But like other important tools you own, it needs to be protected, and it's most effective when used.

4.

Food Allergies and Your Diet

Sensitive or not, we all have to eat, at least at this point in time. And like anyone else, we do love our favorite foods. But as you will learn, the sensitivities of an ultra-sensitive can be like a double-edged sword. That is, not only do we have sensitive emotions, sensitive energies, and keen intuitive skills, we also have sensitive glands and organs, including our digestive tract and our immune system. And for many of us that means we may not always be able to eat all the things we wish all the time.

Not feeling so well after eating dairy? Can't tolerate gluten? Perhaps you still indulge in milk, cheese, wheat, peanuts, tomatoes, even soy. Perhaps you experience muscle aches, headaches, skin rashes, digestive problems, or palpitations after eating some of your favorite foods, or any food. This is not entirely unexpected. Because unlike many of our less sensitive human counterparts, we ultra-sensitives have to be careful, very careful, about what foods and beverages we choose to put into our bodies.

Why? You have food allergies. And lots of them. And ultra-sensitives tend to have more kinds of food reactions and more severe symptoms from these foods than most because--yes, you got it--they are ultra-sensitive. Sensitive to everything.

THE YOUNG BOY WITH FOOD PHOBIAS

There was a young man who grew up in Southern California. He was a picky young man, and a sensitive young man. He was nine years old when he had his first taste of a McDonald's hamburger. He liked his hamburgers very well, but he liked them one way and one way only.

PLAIN and DRY. No ketchup, pickles, no mustard. Everything he ate had to be plain.

But this wasn't just any plain young man. This young man was an ultra-sensitive, but he didn't know that yet. His parents didn't know it either. They were struggling just to find a way to feed and care for him, and their other children. And they fed this young man well on their limited income. But they also let him eat whatever he wanted. Plenty of doughnuts, burgers, sodas, cakes, and pastries. Even fast foods became a regular affair. All was well, for a while, or so they thought.

Now, the other three siblings were not nearly as sensitive. They consumed all the foods they wished without any problems whatsoever. But this young man didn't fare so well. At age fifteen, literally overnight, this young man became very depressed. His whole world suddenly turned upside down. He lost interest in his job at McDonald's, had difficulty studying or concentrating and had trouble engaging in any personal relationships. Even sitting in front of the TV to watch his favorite shows became a painful chore.

He quickly lost his spunk and his will to live. Nothing was enjoyable. It didn't matter whether the food was plain and dry, because he had lost his passion for eating, for all foods.

Yes, young Emil Faithe had become clinically depressed. After dozens of tests and doctors, no one could find anything wrong. But something *was* wrong.

It took thirty years for the young man to figure it out on his own, but he finally did. His longstanding mood issues were the direct result of multiple overwhelming food allergies. And those overwhelming food allergies in this sensitive body had triggered an immune response that ultimately resulted in chemical imbalances in his brain.

Yes, this sensitive got his first taste of a long and sustained plight known as "Ultra-Sensitive Meets Planet Earth."

After working diligently to eliminate the food allergy culprits, namely dairy, wheat, alcohol, tomatoes, sulfites, and fast and processed food additives, he began to return to the world of the living. This resulted in the calming of his inflamed immune system. His moods stabilized, his energy increased, his muscle aches and pains resolved, and his weight balanced. All because he paid attention to what he ate.

I'M BACK

To this day he still watches what he eats, knowing full well that when he doesn't, he may still experience the mood shifts and other symptoms he thought he left far behind. But at least now he knows what he's up against. You should know, too.

Food allergies can cause a wide variety of symptoms, many of them lifelong and disabling. For me, it was depression.

Today, my life is far from plain. It's fantastic. And my hamburgers? These days there's plenty of ketchup, mustard, pickles, and onions on them, and anything else that I'm not allergic to, that makes me happy.

WHAT'S BOTHERING *YOU*?

Most people believe that eating foods that you're allergic to can cause gas, or other digestive symptoms. It can. But remember, for an ultra-sensitive it's not that simple. We experience everything in extremes. For the ultra-sensitive, gas and bloating is the just the beginning of what the wrong foods can do to you. It runs much deeper than that. For ultra-sensitives, food allergy reactions are at the root of some of today's most chronic and debilitating conditions, including depression.

Many of my patients are shocked to learn that their food allergies, and the immune responses that they create, are at the root cause of Lupus, multiple sclerosis, rheumatoid arthritis, and other auto-immune disorders, migraine headaches, diabetes, hypertension, even hormonal and thyroid imbalances, including hot flashes, and more.

And although food allergies may not be the primary cause in every case, they are almost always contributory to the overall health picture.

Symptoms of food allergies:

There are many. This list is not inclusive. Here are just a few:

- Muscle and joint aches
- Mood imbalances
- Anxiety and Anxiousness
- Hyperactivity
- Hypertension
- Headaches
- Digestive problems (gas, diarrhea, constipation, bloating, reflux)
- Insomnia
- Diabetes
- Hormonal imbalances (hot flashes)
- Palpitations
- Weight gain
- Shortness of breath/wheezing
- Skin rashes
- Dry mouth

How do you find out for sure whether you're allergic to a specific food, food group, food additive, or beverage? Two choices. You can either do a meticulous food and beverage elimination diet, one item at a time, or you can go the easy route and find out what you're allergic to all at once, with food allergy testing.

DO I HAVE FOOD ALLERGIES?

You can bet on it. That's because *everyone* has food allergies. It's simply a matter of how many foods you're allergic to and to what degree.

Unfortunately, most mainstream doctors almost never consider food allergies when diagnosing problematic health symptoms. Doctors that do usually recommend a blood test to check them. Unfortunately, blood tests for food allergies often result in false negatives, leading patients to believe they have few or no food allergies and, worse yet, eliminating the potential for solving the health symptom puzzle.

There's a better and more accurate way to test for food allergies: energy testing, or what is referred to as Applied Kinesiology (AK). AK is extremely accurate because it tests for food allergies against your specific energy imprint, or what we call the aura. More important, it does not measure results against a predetermined worldwide standard. It measures results against *your* standard, *your* normal. It's non-invasive and extremely accurate, and the results are immediate. And AK is typically less expensive than traditional testing methods.

Choose the method you prefer to test for your food allergies, using your intuitive means. But whichever way you choose, find a way to learn about what foods and beverages *you're* allergic to. Check with your local holistic practitioner, or contact my office for more information on food allergy testing.

STEVE BELIEVES

A gentleman walked into my office just recently. He had been advised by his allopathic MD to get tested for food allergies. That made sense, since Steve had presented with the classic food allergy symptoms; muscle and joint aches and esophageal reflux and other digestive symptoms. At first, I was quite pleased to hear that an allopathic MD had the foresight to evaluate his patient for food allergies, since this is such a rare event. But then came the surprise.

Steve was flabbergasted at his food allergy results. The blood test results indicated that he did not have any allergies to dairy and tomatoes. This was puzzling since Steve proclaimed that he felt horrible when he ate those particular foods. He couldn't accept the validity of these test results and he asked that I perform the food allergy panel my way, through muscle testing. I was happy to oblige.

Sure enough, when I tested him he proved to be 4+ (the most severe level of reaction) allergic to dairy and tomatoes and to several other foods that the blood tests had shown to be non-reactive. Steve's blood

> tests had indeed reported several critical false negatives. Had Steve followed those results, he would have assumed that he was not allergic to those foods and would have continued to experience food allergy symptoms. Worse yet, he would have likely undergone additional "testing" to find out what was wrong, all futile.
>
> In fact, nothing was wrong. Steve was just an ultra-sensitive with multiple and significant food allergies. He diligently followed the results of the AK food panel testing and stayed clear of dairy and tomatoes and the other allergens, and Steve's muscle aches and digestive symptoms resolved completely over the next few weeks. Yours can too.

I've had dozens of other patients proudly tell me that their allopathic practitioner has proclaimed them to be food-allergy free. That's right. They were told they had NO food allergies. That is, they had no food allergies according to blood tests. That is very curious and concerning, considering that, of the thousands of patients I have tested over the years, I have never found *one* that tested with *no* food allergies.

So please be sure of this: As an ultra-sensitive, you DO have food allergies, and you have more than most people. And you also have more severe reactions to these foods than most people.

DAIRY FAIRY

Almost every one of us was weaned on cow's milk when we came of age, perhaps beginning at age two or three. And for decades we've subjected our sensitive immune system to cow's milk and other dairy products.

Now, years later, the thought of consuming cow's milk is simply out of the question for many ultra-sensitives, unless they're prepared for serious digestive distress, muscle aches, and more. And despite popular belief, the lactose component of milk has little or nothing to do with this allergy. We are allergic to the actual cow proteins in the milk, which means supplementing with lactase enzymes often results in little or no relief of symptoms.

SAY CHEESE

And then there's cheese, the fungus among us we just can't resist. It is one of the most beloved comfort foods around and easily rivals ice cream and chocolate for the number-one spot. In fact, studies show that coming off cheese is more difficult than quitting smoking. Now that says something about our addiction to this marvelous dairy product.

Do I eat cheese? I must confess, yes I do, at times. Do I have uncomfortable symptoms when I eat cheese? You bet. But I choose to consume it in moderation anyway. Why? Because I enjoy it. And I don't believe in or promote the notion of food deprivation. In fact, I vehemently oppose deprivation of any type unless we're doing it as a life-saving effort. And those instances are few and far between. Instead, I recommend multiple doses of the things you enjoy, in moderation, with extra helpings of bliss and joy on a regular basis. So if cheese brings you joy, please continue…in moderation.

DEFY DEPRIVATION

Many ultra-sensitives show up in my office for the first time proudly describing their extreme food deprivation diets. They have come to believe, through the advice of other practitioners, or from information found in a book somewhere or on the web, that the only way to feel better is to give up everything they love to eat. They've given up all sweets, ice cream, chocolate, pastries, chips, caffeine, dairy, wheat, cheese, alcohol and more. Those occasional treats and nibbles of sweets and other beloved snacks are all but gone. Some have chosen to go so far as to give up chicken, beef, turkey, or fish in the name of good health.

Hold on a minute. I beg to differ. Over my years of observation of these types of behaviors I have found that not only is extreme deprivation *not healthy*, it can ultimately lead to significant emotional failure and a multitude of physical symptoms, including depression, insomnia, weight GAIN, immune problems, and more.

Food connoisseurs everywhere, please beware. People who completely deprive themselves of their favorite foods (and other favorite things) are some of the most unhappy, frustrated, and UNHEALTHY people around. They are often more depressed and unhappy than those who partake in moderation. In fact, many in full deprivation have lost their motivation and inspiration and, in extreme cases, even the will to go on.

Yes, you are ultra-sensitive, but you are also still human. For that reason, I don't recommend giving up every food item you love to eat. Want to be a vegetarian or a vegan by choice? That's fine. I honor those personal and moral choices. But I don't recommend going there merely upon the advice of a healthcare practitioner. Extreme food deprivation is not only unnecessary; in some cases it can be downright detrimental. My advice? Enjoy what you eat, in moderation. Just enjoy.

ROSEMARY

Rosemary was a very diligent and stalwart lady. She went by the book on everything. And she took her health very seriously, and was taking extreme measures to maintain her health. When I first met Rosemary, things were indeed extreme. She presented with extreme muscle aches, extreme fatigue, and extreme mood swings. She confessed that she had become very depressed over the last year or so. All of her joy and passion for life was suddenly gone.

It took just a few minutes for me to figure out what was wrong with Rosemary. She had made extreme diet changes in an effort to improve her chronic intestinal upset and to improve the arthritic symptoms that had begun to cripple her.

Yes, like everything else in her life she took her diet changes to extremes, giving up all of her favorite foods and beverages. At first, her muscle aches and pains began to subside, but after several months of stopping all of her favorite foods the muscle aches and digestive problems returned, with vengeance. Not only that, Rosemary became unhappy and downright depressed, so much so that her energy level dropped to the point that she had to give up her beloved Tai Chi. She just didn't have the strength to do it, or the will.

Rosemary and I had a heart-to-heart. I asked her to re-introduce some of her favorite foods, including her beloved provolone cheese and white wine. It took a few weeks, but ultimately Rosemary regained her zest for living, and her joint pain and digestive symptoms disappeared.

Rosemary had finally begun to practice a life of moderation, in her diet choices and in all aspects of her life. She most recently began to teach Tai Chi. And she promised not to push too hard.

IT'S ALL ABOUT BALANCE

We all have choices to make in our lives every day. As ultra-sensitives, we need to be careful not to push anything to extremes, lest our bodies and minds fight back. For an ultra-sensitive, just as for everyone else, feeling healthy and vital is not about joy deprivation, and it's not about over-indulgence. It's about something in between. I call it balance.

When it comes to choosing your foods, be sensible. You want some ice cream? Have it once in a while, just not a large bowlful every day. Do you love cheese? Enjoy some; just don't eat a pizza every day. Follow your intuition and monitor your symptoms, and you'll know what to do. And by all means, keep a good food diary, and make record of the foods and any and all symptoms that arise after eating them, including changes in mood and anxiety levels.

DELAYED REACTIONS

Food allergy reactions can occur at any time after consumption, from just minutes after eating to as much as a week after a single exposure. That's right. Food allergy reactions can be delayed, from several days to a week or more after consuming a particular food or beverage. This is not uncommon and is, in fact, exactly how it works for me and my immune system.

If I have Chinese food, or go to any restaurant that uses soy sauce, spices or other ingredients my body can't handle, I won't know what hit me until three to five days later. That's when my muscle aches and digestive problems kick in. And those may last for a week or more. That can suck the joy out of eating out, if you're not careful. Not fun.

It's true that delayed food reactions can be a bit more challenging to follow and pinpoint, but learning what's been making you feel lousy all of these years is a great reward. So, keep a good food diary and you will eventually find a trend. Then you'll be able to make the needed dietary changes. Then you'll feel better. It's worth it.

Once you've connected the dots, either through food allergy testing or the elimination method, stay clear of the food and beverage culprits for at least six months. This will allow your traumatized immune system to calm down. Once it does, you can begin to slowly bring back the foods you love, one at a time.

WHAT CAN I EAT?

Many people become discouraged when they learn that they're allergic to many of their favorite foods and many of the basic food groups. They often comment, "There's nothing left to eat." In truth, there is plenty that you can eat. It's simply about exploring new choices. Can't eat wheat? Try grains like quinoa, amaranth, or buckwheat. Can't handle cow's milk? Almond milk, rice milk, or any of the nut milks are great and tasty alternatives. So enjoy!

A comprehensive food allergy panel will provide with an accurate picture of not only the foods you're allergic to, but also those foods you are *not* allergic to. Focus on those. You will find that you actually have plenty of healthy and delicious choices. All of those foods and many others are out there in the world and available for your sensitive and discriminating palate.

There really is a whole new world of food choices available to you. It's simply a matter of adjusting some old routines and diet habits and creating new ones that will keep you and your sensitive immune system happy.

Take this simple test:

Which of the following foods do you consume on a daily or regular basis, say, three to five days a week? Write down the numbers that correspond to the foods you eat most often.

1. Cow's milk/cheese
2. Amaranth
3. Soy
4. Ezekiel bread
5. Strawberries
6. Pomegranate
7. Peanuts
8. Sweet potatoes
9. Tomatoes
10. Walnuts
11. Bell peppers (any color)
12. Almond milk
13. Shrimp
14. Salmon
15. Oranges
16. Spelt bread
17. Corn
18. Apple cider vinegar
19. Wheat bread
20. Broccoli

Now, count the number of **odd numbered** selections you eat and compare to the number of **even numbered** selections you eat.

If more than half of your choices are even numbered you are eating a diet that is generally *less* likely to elicit food allergy reactions. If you are eating less than five of the foods that are even numbered, it's *more* likely that food allergies are negatively impacting your health.

In general, the more **odd numbered** choices you make the more likely you are to experience food allergy symptoms, as these foods are classic food allergy triggers in the much of the population.

MAKE A PLAN

Food allergies remain one of the most under-recognized causes for acute and chronic health conditions, and they plague both the ultra-sensitive and the less-sensitive without prejudice. Yet food allergy reactions remain one of the most easily correctable maladies. So take the time to create the perfect diet and nutrition plan based on your unique sensitivities, and you will feel better for it.

And remember, no matter *which* foods you choose to eat each day, enjoy them all with gusto, and without guilt.

5.

Family: Who Are These Strangers?

Ultra-sensitive or not, everybody has a family. We have grown up getting to know these people better than anyone else. They are the people we count on, people who should know us better, and care about us more than anyone else on the planet. Or, maybe not.

But wait. These people are our relatives, our closest kin. They should be nurturing, supportive, kind, understanding, even compassionate. After all, we are related by blood and genetic coding. We share similar traits, blood parents, and eons of cultural lineage. By nature, these people should be willing to do whatever it takes to embrace, defend, and protect us, the ultra-sensitives, under any circumstances.

I'm sorry. In many cases, nothing could be further from the truth. In fact, many ultra-sensitives will tell you straight out that some of their blood relatives are more distant and callous than anyone else they know. Many will go one further, to say that they receive more support and compassion from friends, co-workers, even strangers in the grocery store, than from their own family.

Yes, siblings, even parents, can be competitive, envious and even malicious when they interact with other family members, and especially so when they interact with a family member that is an ultra-sensitive. Unfortunately, when it comes to the relationships between an ultra-sensitive and other members of the family, the term "bad blood" often really does apply.

THICKER THAN *WHAT*?

As many ultra-sensitives have learned, the notion that someone is "blood" does not necessarily mean they're anything like you. In fact, when we try to connect with our closest family members on most any topic, it's often like oil and water.

So who are these people, our family, really? And what are they *really* doing in our lives?

The reality is that family members are no different than any of the other actors in the play we call "life." Everyone has a role to play. These roles were contracted and agreed upon prior to coming into body, designed to help all of us learn our "life lessons" and achieve soul growth. Yet for those of us who are ultra- sensitive and the ultra-perceptive, it may seem almost inconceivable that dysfunctional family members could be here to bring us any good at all. Inhospitable family relationships can leave even the most tolerant ultra-sensitive asking, "What kind of lesson is that?"

I am not suggesting that every family unit is dysfunctional, malicious, or unbalanced. There are many family relationships that are very healthy and supportive. Yours may be one of them. But if members of your family are making you feel uncomfortable, angry, or just plain left out, you're not alone. Yet you certainly may feel that way.

A FAMILY OF ONE

If you haven't already figured this out, not everybody in the family unit of an ultra-sensitive *is* a sensitive. Quite the contrary. In many cases you will be the only one in the family who gets what it means to be sensitive. Many ultra-sensitives say that they feel alone and lonely within their family units, and often describe themselves as being "their own family." They often go so far as to refer to themselves as the black sheep of the family.

But perhaps they have it backwards. It may well be that the ultra-sensitive member of the family is actually the *white sheep,* the soft, gentle, compassionate one. We're often the dreamer, the introvert, the one dealing with the symptoms of what the medical community likes to call ADHD or

ADD. Often, we are the ones crying all the time, or hiding away in our rooms, even in closets and under beds. We may even make invisible friends and create exciting new places to drift off to in our minds (our reality) so that we can find solace and serenity. Why? Because we simply find it difficult and painful to relate to the rest of the world.

We're often perceived as the "weak ones," the ones that do not have adequate social skills. We tend to be shy, quiet, thoughtful, gentle mannered, overly considerate, and ultra diligent. Yet, in the eyes of our family mates, we're often just plain weird. They don't get us and we don't get them. And that's okay.

Despite what we may believe, however, many "insensitive" family members may look at us as though we *are* the "black sheep," an embarrassment to our parents, siblings, and other family members. Well, they need to get over it. You're exactly who you're supposed to be, doing exactly what you came here to do. So please carry on!

Symptoms of Black Sheep Syndrome (BSS):

Do any of these sound familiar?

- Cry at the drop of a hat
- Introverted, a person of few words
- People call you "complex"
- Ultra-capable
- Ultra-diligent
- Often feel the need to hide away in your special place
- Poor social skills
- Soft-spoken
- Love to paint, write, draw, dance, sing, and be creative in any way
- Have invisible friends
- Don't like to think, or think way too much
- Don't like the same foods as the rest of the family
- Have multiple food allergies
- Feel alone or lonely no matter who you are with
- Lack friends or are a loner at school or social events

- Find confrontation horribly painful and undesirable
- Have a constant, burning desire to help others.

TIM

Tim was the classic ultra-sensitive. He grew up as the oldest of three children and was ultra diligent and ultra capable. From day one he felt like the caretaker of the rest of the family, including his parents. From age seven on, Tim was left alone to care for his two younger siblings.

But Tim wasn't like anybody else his age. He had difficulty interacting with others, including his schoolmates. He didn't partake in the usual activities of kids his age. An A-student and a deep thinker, Tim just couldn't relate. He felt quite alone no matter where he was or what he did. He seemed to live in his own little world.

Tim grew to love music and became a masterful chef. He could cook up an entire party with his eyes closed. He was also an amazing event planner. Tim could visualize an entire event from start to finish, from the colors to the foods, to the party favors, to the music and décor. And he was quite the intuitive. Yes, Tim could sense the truth about anything, or anybody anywhere he went.

What Tim couldn't do was function in the outside world. When he hit his forties it became increasingly difficult for him to hold down a job. He became increasingly fearful of open spaces and being around people, to the point that he literally had to run in and out of grocery stores to do his shopping, to avoid having panic attacks. Tim just could not be around other people.

Many of his co-workers, friends, and even family members began to stay clear of Tim when possible. In hush-hush conversations, his unusual behavior became the hot topic around the kitchen, and around the water cooler. It seemed that the more people ridiculed him the worse his phobias became.

The emotional stress and ridicule took a toll. He began to develop chronic insomnia and more frequent and intense panic attacks, until he became addicted to his anti-anxiety and insomnia medicines. Tim was indeed an extreme sensitive that no one understood, and the perennial "black sheep".

It took several years, but Tim's siblings finally began to understand what he was going through. They eventually began to change their demeanor around him. His parents, who had long known Tim was "different," slowly began to accept him for who he was: a misunderstood ultra-sensitive.

When the time came for the family to make amends with the black sheep of the family, Tim had made peace with them, as well. He forgave his family members and began to spend more time helping them cope with their own life challenges and lessons. As his parents aged they needed more help to get along. So, too, did his two siblings from time to time. He provided that, and was there for them. In the process he came to realize that by "giving back" to the family who once shunned him, he was able to overcome many of his own shortcomings and find happiness in his ultra-sensitive existence.

He went on to help others learn the lessons they needed to learn. Indeed, Tim taught them what they needed to know, not just about him, but about themselves. He was content with this resolution. He's enjoyed being the caretaker of all who would allow it, and to this day guides others on their path of enlightenment and sensitivity.

HELLO, MAY I HELP YOU?

These challenging family relationships can be quite traumatic to the ultra-sensitive, often doing permanent damage to our confidence and self-worth, and ultimately reshaping our entire life paths. I've had many ultra-sensitive go so far as to say that their closest family members have "sabotaged" and "undermined" their life potential. That's quite a statement, and it seems to be an unjust reward for the ultra-sensitive who often simply wants to help others. So why does it seem that the ultra-sensitive is being punished for being sensitive?

Many spiritual "purists" would argue that it was all meant to be, that is was for the higher good; that we chose these players and situations for our soul evolution. Ten years ago I might have agreed with some of that. But now, having survived malicious family shenanigans of my own over the years, I sometimes find that concept hard to swallow.

Are there broader and deeper agendas at play? Perhaps. The fact remains, many of our less sensitive family members carry considerable envy, and even unspoken anger, toward their ultra-sensitive relatives.

In many ways it seems to be the same old story: dark versus light. And although much of this age-old phenomenon may seem diluted within the context of family values, it seems that is does still exist. Less-sensitive family members usually don't know *why* they want to sabotage your life, they just do.

SIGNIFICANT OTHER?

What happens when an ultra-sensitive gets involved in a relationship with a less-sensitive partner? Does the house explode? Does their hair catch on fire? Or do they live happily ever after? It depends on the karmic event that is being played out. These types of mixed couple relationships are not necessarily doomed to failure.

Like any other relationship, it's a matter of balance. It's a matter of give and take. If the ultra-sensitive gives and everyone else takes, the relationship will likely fail. If a healthy balance can be established, and if a mutual understanding and respect prevails, the relationship has a much better chance of survival. Don't give up on your relationship without making reasonable attempts to balance and nurture it. Holistic emotional counseling sessions can be very beneficial to this end.

However, if the ultra-sensitive remains in a relationship that is unbalanced and un-nurturing, that stifles expression and creativity, which does not allow for mutual respect and understanding, the ultra-sensitive will likely develop physical or emotional ailments that may ultimately spell their demise. Health conditions like diabetes, high cholesterol, weight issues and depression are likely to develop as the years pass.

As to *how* a stifled relationship can manifest into a specific ailment, I defer to Dr. Faithe's Law of Energy Attraction:

What you hold on to will eventually make you sick.

As to *which* illness will likely manifest, that will be determined by the genetic tendencies of the ancestors.

It's true that these types of relationship challenges can create similar problems among less-sensitives. Yet ultra-sensitives typically experience significant health symptoms much sooner than do the less-sensitive, and these symptoms often become more severe and more resistant to treatment, unless an emotional clearing is performed to release the stifling.

Symptoms of a stifled sensitive relationship:

- Depression
- Headaches
- Bouts of unprovoked crying
- Lupus, Rheumatoid Arthritis, MS, Chronic Fatigue or any other autoimmune disorder
- Diabetes
- Exhaustion
- Apathy
- Insomnia
- High Blood Pressure
- Joint and Muscle Aches
- Skin Rashes
- Bipolar Disorder
- ADHD

JENNIFER

Jennifer was forty-two, very intelligent, eloquent, and a professor at the local university. She was ultra-diligent, ultra-responsible, and a very structured individual, but above all she was an ultra-sensitive. Unfortunately, she was also in a committed relationship to a man who was, in short, insensitive to ultra-sensitives. Jennifer confessed that at times her husband had gone so far as to ridicule her for some of her beliefs, and was all but closed shut when it came to matters of spirit.

Jennifer had been diagnosed with the mainstream label of Rheumatoid Arthritis, and she was in constant pain, day and night. When we first visited she was in great pain; at eight on a scale of ten. All of her joints were hot and inflamed, especially her knees and ankles. She had been prescribed a moderate dose of prednisone, a potent steroid medicine, to control the pain and inflammation. But her pain relief was never complete and she was experiencing side effects from the drug: swelling of the face, ankles and feet, and blood sugar changes.

But the steroid medicine was only a cover-up. It was not addressing the true cause of her symptoms. You see, Jennifer's symptoms were the result of her years of poor diet choices. She had been eating many of the foods she was severely allergic to; tomatoes, wheat, cheese, the usual suspects, and these were triggering a profound immune response, which resulted in her joint pain and inflammation.

Jennifer completed the food allergy panel in the office and eliminated the food culprits. I started her on a potent digestive enzyme, fish oil, and several other natural immune modulators. Over the following four months her symptoms began to improve dramatically. By the end of six months her immune system balanced completely. She was able to taper off of the steroids, and all of her joint pain was gone, except for her knees.

Things seemed to be better, but not enough. I sensed there was something else at play here. Something else needed to be revealed. It took a regression session to find it.

During the regression Jennifer was able to recall a life where she practiced as a prominent psychic medium. After she had returned to full awareness, Jennifer went on to tell me that indeed her mother was a prominent psychic medium in this life, and that she herself was one in a long line of psychic mediums on her maternal side. As it turns out, Jennifer was the next in line. But she hadn't yet used this gift.

After further discussion, she revealed that her husband was not open to her psychic skills and wanted to hear nothing more about it. That was eleven years ago. Jennifer had been stifled, unable to express her gifts. Yes, her powerful pent-up energies were the root cause of her inflammation. Her ankle pain and swelling was the result of not being able to express her true calling, her life path.

Jennifer got the picture. She worked to resolve the blocks in her spousal relationship and began seeing clients as a psychic medium. And she was remarkably successful. She phoned me about a year later to tell me that her pain and inflammation had completely disappeared.

Jennifer had been successful in overcoming the influences of a stifling spousal relationship. You can be successful, too.

TAKE A PEEK

Take a look at all of your current family relationships: mother, father, sister, brother, aunts, uncles, significant other...Go ahead. Take a close look.

- Do these relationships nurture and support you?
- Do they make you feel important?
- Do they build your self-esteem and confidence?
- Do they allow you to be yourself, to express yourself as the ultra-sensitive you are?

Or, rather:

- Do you feel suffocated and stifled?
- Do you feel controlled by their energies, either consciously or subconsciously?
- Do you feel a constant low level of apprehension?
- Do you feel like a prisoner in your own family unit?

Go ahead ponder those questions for a few moments. I'll wait...

If your family makes you feel like a stranger or an outsider, if they hold you down and strangle your confidence and self-esteem, if you feel a sense of dread when you're around them or when you think of them, you're within their energetic grasp. And that's not healthy. That kind of energy control can keep you from doing what you came here to do, and from the fully productive life you've been dreaming about.

How to come to terms with your relationships:

- Drop the guilt. The fact that they're family doesn't necessarily mean they're looking out for your best interests. Accept that and go on living your life your way.
- Set boundaries. Don't allow yourself to be abused physically, emotionally, mentally, or spiritually.
- If you feel like you're being ignored or abused, open a dialogue with the parties involved. If more than one family member is involved, speak to them separately, one by one. Stay clear of the "kangaroo court." Don't push it. Find the right time, the right place, *and* the right words and tone for these conversations.
- Keep the conversation positive and open-ended. State your concerns and describe the specific behavioral changes you're looking for. "I would like more respect for who I am, even if you don't agree with what I do."
- Avoid confrontation. If the conversation escalates out of control, don't attempt to "win" the battle. Just walk away. At least now you have a clear understanding of who and what you're dealing with, and so do they.
- If all else fails, understand that you've done the healthy thing, the right thing. You've taken the high road and done all you can to improve the relationship. At the end of the day, no matter what words or emotions were exchanged, you've regained their respect and salvaged your dignity, and your self-esteem. Those are always yours to keep.

You are an ultra-sensitive. And just like less-sensitives, you need support and nurturing, just a lot more of it, to keep you going. If your family makes you feel like a stranger, or worse, and reconciliation has failed, make the emotional break.

CUT THE CORDS

That doesn't mean that you don't love these people. It doesn't mean that you must get a divorce, or break up with a significant other, or disown a family member (although these options are available to you). It simply means you are going to energetically break their emotional hold over you.

Try this simple exercise:

- Locate a quiet and private space where you can sit or recline.
- Close your eyes and take a slow cleansing breath in through your nose. Then another. Then relax.
- Now, identify the person with whom you wish to cut the cords that bind you. See their face and feel their energies. Take your time. That's it. You've got 'em in your sights.
- Envision a one-inch diameter golden cord attached from your heart chakra to their heart chakra. Sense whether there are other cords that bind you to this individual. In many cases, we are "corded" over large parts of the body, if not the entire body. Trust what you sense.
- Envision a large pair of golden scissors (go with me on this). Now, with the power of your mind, begin to cut the cords you have identified, one by one. Take your time. Make sure you've cut all of them.
- *You are not cutting ties or ending your connection with the individual per se. You are only cutting the negative emotional and energetic cords that are keeping you down and holding you back.*
- You'll know that you're done cutting when you sense that an intense heaviness has left your body. You may feel like crying. Please do. You may feel like laughing. Please do. No matter what you feel like doing, know that you have freed yourself from their influence over you.
- Thank the individual for the lessons this connection, has brought you and bless them as you release their hold over you.
- When you feel that you're done, take several more cleansing breaths through your nose. Relax and allow the cleansing to fully integrate over the next few minutes, or more.

You may repeat this procedure for each person with whom you wish to be energetically freed.

As you will find, cord cutting can create quite an emotional release; hence you may choose to perform only one clearing per day. Or you may choose to do more. Just make sure you are emotionally and physically prepared to handle each de-cording session before you begin. Use your intuition.

YOU GOTTA LOVE 'EM

No matter what else we may feel about these people we call family, they are still your family, and they have an unmistakable connection to you even if that connection seems misguided. Deep down they know who you are, even if they have no clue at the surface level. They may not consciously understand the unique challenges you're dealing with as an ultra-sensitive. They may not understand you at all. Yet at the soul level they love you deeply, even if they don't show it. And you love them. Accept and acknowledge this truth.

The family is an integral part of every civilization, including ours. As we continue to evolve as ultra-sensitive we gain an even higher insight into the role of the family as we know it. As we do, we continue to clear away the mystique that family plays in our lives. Then we can begin to resolve our differences, no matter what they are. Just trust that some differences will be resolved and healed quickly and easily in this lifetime, while others will find a different way of working themselves out, perhaps in other times. No matter which, it's all part of the Plan.

6.

Being Invisible

By now you've recognized that the life of an ultra-sensitive is not always easy. We face some curious and fascinating challenges, indeed. One of the most curious quirks that I have encountered is this one: No matter where we go or what we do, we're often ignored and overlooked by others. It's almost as though we're, well, invisible. If you consider the high frequency of our energy vibration, which is the hallmark of an ultra-sensitive, it makes perfect sense. The truth is, in many cases we *are* energetically invisible to others.

Now, being energetically invisible or undetectable to others may sound like a good thing, especially if you're looking to retire, or retreat into a spiritual setting, or just plain hide away. But many ultra-sensitives aren't quite ready for that yet. For many ultra-sensitives, especially healers and teachers, work involves interacting with others on a daily basis. We've got important things to do, and for many of us that requires direct contact with the public at large. Invisibility is not an option.

Yes, being energetically invisible to the rest of the world can make daily living quite challenging, and frustrating. It can also make our struggle to get our fair share of all the good in life seem unfair.

FLIP ON YOUR BLINKER

Has this ever happened to you? You're in line at the checkout counter of the grocery store. You carefully navigate your cart to be the next in line when someone nearly mows you down with a cartful of Spam. They don't even bat an eye as they scrape past you with their cart. "Excuse me. Hellooo. I'm standing right over here!"

Or maybe you're looking for a parking space in a parking lot packed with cars. Someone is about to pull out, so you gently maneuver yourself toward the spot. Then out of nowhere a car zooms in and cuts you off. "Excuse me; I've been waiting patiently over here".

Just days before going to press, my wife and I were waiting for a seat in one of the popular restaurants in town. We were scoping out two seats at the crowded bar for almost twenty minutes, in fact we were standing right next to them. The moment the seats were vacated, we moved in. Out of nowhere another couple flew over, cut us off, and took our seats, without so much as a blink of the eye. Not a peep. We were definitely invisible, and very frustrated.

The stories go on and on. What's yours? Are *you* invisible?

Take the invisibility test:

- Do you often feel like the fifth wheel in a meeting or a social event?
- When you speak up, do people look at you strangely and wonder who you are?
- When people talk to you do you feel like they're talking to somebody else?
- Does it seem like, no matter how great your idea is, nobody cares?
- When you go to a family event do you feel like everyone is looking right through you?
- When you're involved in a competitive event like a card game, a sport, or a contest, do you feel like you're not even there?

If you answered yes to at least *one* of these questions, you are an ultra-sensitive, and sometimes invisible to others. But you already knew that. If you answered yes to more than one of them, you can be sure your energy imprint is indeed too high to be recognized by many. It's almost as though you're on one planet and the rest of the world is on another.

MARY

I met Mary at a health food store I was visiting. They were hosting an energy healing event that day. People were milling around the store waiting to be worked on by one of several energy workers, Reiki practitioners, and the like. I had never had Reiki so I decided to sign up.

Three of the energy workers were booked solid. They had clients scheduled throughout the day. But Mary stood quietly and alone at her sign up sheet. She had only a few signups and no one seemed to be drawn to her. Of course, I was.

We began the session. Her Reiki energy completely balanced my energy in a way I'd never experienced before. Although smaller in stature and very gentle, she had a magical energy about her, and very powerful. Her work was nothing short of amazing.

Mary's was clearly an ultra-sensitive, unlike some of the other "energy workers" there that day. Her energy was indeed very light and high-vibrational, so much so that Mary was invisible to many. But not to me. I could feel her gentle, sensitive energy when I walked through the door.

We had a few moments to chat after our session was complete, during which she nearly broke down in tears. She proceeded to tell me how slow her business had been, despite the fact that others like her were constantly busy. She went on to describe instance after instance where she was overlooked throughout her life: in school, in job situations, in social events.

When I got home that evening, I began to think about Mary's story and realized how amazingly similar it was to my own. I, too, had been overlooked, ridiculed, picked last, if at all. I, too, rarely spoke out when taken advantage of. And like Mary, I had long been uncertain what my life path was all about, or whether I'd ever be recognized for anything important in my life.

Several months after our visit, Mary called me. She told me she had left town to take care of a sick family member. While doing so she was chastised by the very person she was caring for, despite the fact that she gave up her career and friends to take care of this person. It seemed that the cycle of invisibility just would not end. But one day, suddenly, it did. Mary was called to return to her home state to head up a group of light workers in a new Healing Center. Mary was finally recognized, and she was able to finally achieve her life-long dream.

Following Mary's journey helped me bring a very important lesson to others, and to myself. And here it is:

It's not important who recognizes you for what; it's only important that you recognize yourself, for who you are and for what you came here to do.

It was a powerful lesson, one that I carry with me to this day, in my practice and in my life.

As for me…Well, the journey continues. I'm not picked last anymore, because nowadays I get to choose *whom I want* to be picked by. And you can too.

SEE YOU THERE?

Having undetectable energy and being overlooked on your ultra-sensitive journey may seem to be an inappropriate reward for the powerful work we are doing during your mission on the planet, but it's simply another sign that ultra-sensitives are not like everyone else. Yet, the prospect of energy invisibility is but one of the unique conundrums that an ultra-sensitive may experience.

Because of our unique energy make-up and our high-vibrational energy signature, ultra-sensitives are subject to a number of unusual and sometimes unexplainable energy phenomena. Another of those phenomena worthy of mention and important to your existence on the planet is *translocation,* being in more than one place at one time.

Is it possible that you could be in more than place at one time? You'd be surprised, or maybe not.

TOM TRAVEL

Tom was a self-acknowledged sensitive; a hard working, diligent man with a great job and even a better reputation as an upstanding citizen, father, and husband. He worked in a grocery store and was well know and admired by many of his co-workers. Tom had distinctive facial features, including a uniquely shaped goatee, and he had an unmistakable look about him.

Tom believed in many facets of spirit work and practiced, even honed many of his intuitive gifts on a regular basis. In fact, in his secret life, unbeknownst to all of his work colleagues, he was quite a powerful healer in his own right. But nothing could have prepared him for this next adventure.

It was break time. Tom headed to the bank that was in the grocery store to make a deposit. He and the teller, Larry, had become excellent acquaintances over the years.

Larry barked out, “Hey, I saw you driving down Tatum Boulevard yesterday.” Tom sparked up. “You did? That’s not possible.” Larry insisted. “It was definitely you. I know what you look like. It was definitely you.”

Tom was flabbergasted. There was no way that he could have been driving in that location at that time on that day. Tom had been working all that day at this very supermarket.

The dialogue became intense. Tom assured Larry there was no way he could have been there at the time or place Larry described. Larry was adamant, almost chagrinned that Tom was arguing with him.

“It was you, Tom, I know you and I know your car. You were driving your car and you waved when you saw me.” Tom shook his head in disbelief, and then finally conceded. What in the world was going on?

No, this wasn’t an episode out of the *Twilight Zone*. Or maybe it was. Neither Tom nor Larry could explain the phenomena. Larry shrugged it off as Tom’s memory lapse. It wasn’t quite that simple for Tom, who quickly realized that something extraordinary had occurred on that day, driving down Tatum Boulevard. Tom *had* been in two places at one time. It could not be explained any other way. It was unexplainable.

But for Tom, no further explanation was necessary. He understood and accepted the possibility that perhaps he *was* able to reside in multiple places at one time. After all, Tom was indeed an open-minded ultra-sensitive and a metaphysician, and a powerful one at that, and this event was his powerful awakening to the reality of translocation.

OUT-OF-BODY EXPERIENCES

Our unique makeup of energies opens the ultra-sensitive to a host of potential scientifically unexplainable phenomena. Out of Body Experience (OBE) is yet another.

Do you ever wake up in the morning feeling exhausted? Perhaps you feel as though you've traveled far away from your physical being during the night. Well, likely you have. Many refer to this process of leaving the body as astral traveling or soul projection, or an OBE. Call it what you will, this idea that we leave our bodies while we are still alive (and you are alive) is a common but unrecognized phenomena for many people, and is especially common for ultra-sensitives. And for many, this phenomenon can be a very frightening and unusual experience, to say the least.

We are all capable of having OBE's, but for ultra-sensitives it can almost be a way of life. Where we go and what we are trying to accomplish during these extra-corporal activities is a subject of much debate. Yet nonetheless they seem to be an important part of our lives. And it's true. Most everybody, sensitive or not, leaves their body while in an unconscious state while asleep. It occurs almost like clockwork. But what about the daytime? Is it possible that we leave our bodies without our knowledge during the day, while we are conscious? The answer is yes. Many ultra-sensitives have indeed reported experiencing OBE's *during the waking hours* while going about their daily business.

Has this ever happened to you? You're sitting in a meeting or gathered with a group of people, minding your own business, when suddenly you feel as though you just woke up. You just "snapped back" into your body. What just happened? Were you daydreaming, or did you leave your body for a moment or two? The answer might surprise you.

I've had many ultra-sensitives tell stories about suddenly re-awakening during their normal daily events, not knowing where they had had gone, and losing track of periods of time. It's simply as though they had left their bodies, and then suddenly snapped back.

CAR 54, WHERE ARE YOU?

I received a panicked call from one such person who was literally driving down one of the main streets in her hometown with her young daughter when suddenly she experienced a flash of light. The next thing she knew, her car was traveling down the same street in the opposite direction. She was completely fine, and so was her daughter. Yes, she had been driving safely, just suddenly in the opposite direction for no apparent reason. She was out of breath and astonished, but she was fine.

She went on to describe a sense that she had gone somewhere, to another dimension during that period of time, which apparently had only lasted three minutes. Where, what, and how remained a mystery. What wasn't a mystery was the fact that this ultra-sensitive had been experiencing OBE's since she was a child, but none while she was driving. Until now.

IT'S ALL GOOD

Having the ability to control the projection of our energy fields is just the tip of the iceberg for ultra-sensitives. We possess many gifts, talents and abilities, most, if not all, unrecognized by mainstream scientists and scholars. And though they are not publicly acknowledged as reality, Hollywood has capitalized on many of them to feed the hungry imaginations of the masses.

There have been and continue to be a number of mainstream TV shows based on these types of notions: Star Trek, Twilight Zone, Jumper, Heroes, and others. They feature people who can snap back to the past or the future, and then return to the present, people who can be in one place and also in another. Fact or fiction? You decide.

The fact is, as ultra-sensitives we all have these capabilities. Many have recognized the calling and have chosen to hone their gifts and use them in their daily adventures. Others have chosen not to go there, either because they are fearful or they have not yet recognized their capabilities. Until now.

Are these unexplainable accounts fodder for another great sci-fi series? Perhaps. But until then, understand they are part of the unique energetic makeup of the ultra-sensitive.

7.

Healthcare for the Sensitive

We all need healthcare from time to time. But when it comes to healthcare for the ultra-sensitive, the methods to heal the masses are not always applicable. And in many cases, employing mainstream methods to heal the ultra-sensitive can actually make things worse. Much worse.

First of all, our organs: our entire being is so much different than our less-sensitive counterparts. Besides making us more susceptible to the effects of environmental toxins found in our food, water and air, as well as chemicals and other toxins, it also opens the door for the manifestation of a host of unusual physical and emotional symptoms. Our unique makeup also makes diagnosing imbalances a real challenge, as you will see. Secondly, ultra-sensitives respond differently to medicines and other interventions offered by the traditional healthcare system. All this can leave the weary ultra-sensitive wondering how and where to seek out healthcare when the need arises.

BREAK THE MOLD

Much of the current allopathic healthcare system is very structured and very cookie-cutter. There's one box and everyone has to fit into it. Well, that doesn't work for ultra-sensitives. Our bodies and minds have a different operating system than most everyone else. Even our organs, each with their own unique energy frequency or signatures, operate differently than most. Ultra-sensitives are indeed wired quite differently than everybody else.

That can make choosing healthcare options a very confusing and challenging experience. It's also why traditional healthcare methods and therapies often don't work for ultra-sensitives (or even for some less-sensitives). Not only are these methods often ineffective, they often mask the true cause of symptoms, and in many cases can actually complicate the healing process. Why is that?

ANTIQUATED MEDICINE

We send people to the moon (they say). We can split the atom (is that a good thing?). We can clone human body parts and even whole people (Uh oh). So it would follow, then, that we should be much more advanced in our ability to figure out, diagnose, the root cause of any symptom within the human body. Shouldn't we?

But our healthcare systems are dated, and in many cases operate under methods of thinking and healing that are thousands of years old. You would think that this is a good thing; tried and proven healing techniques. Not so. Our physical, emotional, spiritual, and mental bodies are much more advanced and evolved than they were back then. They're different now. And the rules that applied then, don't necessarily apply now. So what are your options for healing in the world of modern allopathic healthcare?

THIS WON'T HURT A BIT

Surgery and pills are the rule of the day. But cutting out body parts unnecessarily can throw your body's entire energy system into a tizzy. That's because all of our organs are designed to work in harmony, in synchrony with one another. Removing any one of them throws the others out of balance, often creating new lifelong problems.

I'm not suggesting that in certain circumstances surgery isn't beneficial or lifesaving. It can be. In cases of accidents or traumas these extreme measure are necessary to save a life. Rather, I'm suggesting that the medical community at large may be too hasty when it comes to cutting things out. Two good examples of surgical excess are the hysterectomy (surgical removal of the female reproductive organs) and the cholecystectomy (surgical removal of the gallbladder). These are being performed in record numbers, and often without fully exploring non-surgical options or prevention techniques.

THE HIGH ESTROGEN CRISIS

The media has done a fine job of heightening the awareness of hot flashes and osteoporosis in women. Yes, these are annoying and uncomfortable health maladies, and usually the result of *low* estrogen levels. However, the unspoken real pandemic is women running around with *high* estrogen levels in their ultra-sensitive systems. Over time these high levels will create fibroid cysts, changes to the endometrial lining, and if left unchecked (and if genetically inclined) can ultimately lead to breast or ovarian cancer.

High circulating estrogen levels are a far greater issue than low estrogen levels since this can lead to life-threatening health challenges.

High estrogen levels are the leading cause of endometriosis, ovarian cysts, fibrocystic breasts, breast cancer and other serious health challenges. In fact, if one were to go back and examine estrogen levels in patients with these conditions, one would find a clear and distinct correlation between their high estrogen levels and their ailment.

What's even more alarming is that removing the affected female organs does *not* correct the high estrogen levels that created the symptoms in the first place. In my years of following these cases, women, especially ultra-sensitive women, who have had hysterectomies *still have high circulating estrogen levels*, just as they did before surgery. That's because the actual causes of these high levels were never addressed.

Often these women have been taking potent estrogen supplementation with products like Premarin, Estrace (estradiol), Activella and Prempro. Even oral birth control pills can contribute heavily to the high estrogen crisis. Pesticides and other environmental toxins may also play an important role in high estrogen, and should be addressed through dietary precautions.

HEAL THE PAIN

But more than that, high estrogen levels have much to do with unresolved emotional and relationship issues. Simply stated:

***Over-nurturing* others while *under-nurturing* one's self creates a unique cascade of events within the body that ultimately results in high estrogen levels.**

Unfortunately, these are areas of healing that most allopathic physicians do not explore at all. If emotional factors remain uncorrected, estrogen levels will remain high and create the same problems all over again.

The real solution to the high estrogen crisis is to eliminate the cause of high estrogen, using natural methods, not to remove the results. (See Part II: *How to Manage Hormonal Imbalances and Fibroid Cysts*)

THE PROGESTERONE LOW-DOWN

For those women who have had their female organs removed courtesy of a hysterectomy, you now face a new hormonal paradox: *progesterone* imbalances.

The commonly overlooked reality is that women who have had a hysterectomy, complete or partial will have, *without fail,* low progesterone levels, unless they are properly supplemented. Do you have low progesterone levels? If you experience intractable weight gain, migraine headaches, hot flashes, mood swings, low libido, thyroid imbalances, or more, more than likely you do.

So many ultra-sensitive women show up in my office with one, usually many, of the above symptoms, and with low, usually very low, progesterone levels. The good news is that progesterone can be replenished easily through supplementation with topical progesterone cream, available without a prescription. If you are an ultra-sensitive woman, or any woman who has experienced a hysterectomy, I urge you to get your hormones checked and rebalanced promptly. You *will* feel better.

JUST BREAK IT

As you can see, solving the hormonal health puzzle for ultra-sensitive and less-sensitives alike can be tricky business. Every woman is uniquely different and requires careful attention to resolve her specific hormonal symptoms. For the ultra-sensitive woman, the challenge can be even more daunting, due to increased sensitivity to hormonal and nutritional supplements. But it most certainly can be accomplished, and should be. That's because hormonal imbalances can wreak havoc on your wellbeing and your ability to cope, and flourish, during these energetically challenging times.

Yes, you *can* avoid the knife and potent and dangerous prescription estrogen pills. And you *can* restore your vim and vigor. If you need help getting started, seek the guidance of a qualified holistic practitioner, or contact my office. Do it soon. Do it now.

THE GALL OF YOU

Gallbladder disease is rampant, among the young and the mature alike. Symptoms of gallbladder imbalances include right upper quadrant pain, indigestion, chest pain, acid reflux, and other digestive symptoms. Poor diet choices, weight issues, life stressors, and liver congestion (often due to pent-up anger and resentment) can contribute to the formation of gallstones which often go undetected despite the use of "advanced" imagery such as MRI or sonogram. Over time these stones will clog the bile ducts, and in many cases eventually create a gallbladder attack. If you show up in the ER with these symptoms, there's a good chance that your gallbladder will be surgically removed.

But you can escape the knife with a little bit of prevention in the form of diet and supplements. Simple holistic techniques and natural medicines are available that can reduce gallbladder inflammation and help breakdown and eliminate gallstones, thereby solving the problem without the need for surgery.

Ultra-sensitives need their gallbladders. We all do. Once it's out you can't put it back. And life without your gallbladder can lead to life-long digestive issues and more. (See Part II: *How to Manage Gallbladder Problems*)

KATHY HAD SOME GALL

Kathy was a twenty-five year old ultra-sensitive who showed up in my office complaining of acid reflux, bloating, and general GI upset. She also complained of a vague gnawing pain in her upper right quadrant, which had been going on for several years. At first look, I sensed she was having major gastrointestinal inflammation. Yes, she had multiple food allergies, but something else was going on. And I was going to find it.

I performed my usual evaluation, asking the usual probing questions. Half way through our discussion, she piped up and said, "Oh, and by the way, I had my gallbladder removed two years ago." That was the confirmation I needed to hear. Kathy was clearly not digesting fats, and many of her other food stuffs, because her gallbladder was no longer available.

I started her on a digestive enzyme designed for those without gallbladders, and a potent probiotic blend. Within ten days Kathy's GI symptoms had improved dramatically, but not disappeared completely. She still complained of pain in the area where her gallbladder had once resided. It was the phantom pain, which is quite common after gallbladder removal.

On her next visit we explored her lifestyle a little further. As it turned out, Kathy, a stout, powerful-looking yet sensitive woman, was a gifted healer. The problem was, not only was she *not* practicing in her field of hands-on-healing, her day job as a parole officer required her to work with many energetically challenging people. As it turns out, Kathy had been a parole officer for several years prior to her gallbladder surgery.

Under a state of light relaxation we discovered that her parole work grated heavily on her energy, more than she ever realized. She also confessed to being angry at the system, a system which forced her to work overtime almost every day. This left no time or energy to practice her healing work, the work she adored. Yet she never spoke up about it. Like many other ultra-sensitives, she was ultra diligent and ultra responsible. She just put up with it. And all the while her energy, and specifically her gallbladder, was " boiling over." Translation? "The gall of them, to take advantage of my good nature like that!" Kathy's inability to say no, to stand up for what is right and fair, had built up gallstones over a several year period, ultimately resulting in an acute gallbladder attack.

Kathy got the message loud and clear. She began to speak what was on her mind, in her work relationships, personal relationships, and all aspects of her life. No more grudges were held.

It took about a year, but Kathy's phantom gall pain faded away. She left her parole job to pursue work in the Forest Service where she could hone her healing gifts every day on the ready and willing bounties of nature.

HIGH TECH DIAGNOSES, LOW TECH TREATMENT

Modern healthcare brags about fancy machines and expensive, uncomfortable diagnostic procedures. And they charge you well for them. Yet, once you are diagnosed, the treatment options they offer seem no further advanced than they were forty years ago. Your options still remain pills or surgery, with no breakthrough cures for any disease. And for the ultra-sensitives, those options are just not enough.

Not only that, most every allopathic healing modality consists of nothing more than squelching the symptom, shoving them back inside. And that's not healthy. Why? As we've learned, what you hold onto will eventually make you sick. Indeed, burying the symptoms with pills can actually create new and even more significant problems, especially for the ultra-sensitive.

OUCH!

To make matters worse, many of the diagnostic techniques seem as antiquated as they were in the early 1900's; some seem even downright cruel and barbaric at times.

Had a colonoscopy lately? Not fun. A mammogram? Painful and often inconclusive. Or perhaps you've had the privilege of having your back riddled with needles containing dozens of the items you're allergic to, just to have your sensitive immune system sent into orbit for years to come. There's got to be a better way.

Most of the patients who end up in my office have been through it all. They've been through the traditional healthcare ringer. They've had every test imaginable, and some that aren't. They've spent thousands of dollars of their own money, and in some cases hundreds of thousands of the insurance company's money (which, by the way, is our money) just to come away without answers or solutions. Why is that?

You must find the underlying cause!

Pills and surgery do not address the underlying causes of symptoms. That's because the underlying cause is almost always buried in chronic, unresolved emotional issues, or overlooked and undiagnosed diet and nutrition issues, or lifestyle issues such as smoking, stress, environmental toxicities, and food allergies. Balancing the health of the ultra-sensitive absolutely requires that these issues be addressed and resolved.

All the pills on the planet won't get it done. If you really want to get better, and stay better, find a practitioner who can work with your energies, your nutrition, your lifestyle, and your emotions. Balance these and authentic healing can begin, and you will feel better.

MONICA

Monica, a spry fifty-two year old woman, came to see me for her unrelenting menopausal symptoms. It seemed like a routine case. After a full review, I adjusted her diet and started her on a simple hormone balancing regimen. Over the next few weeks, her hot flashes subsided, her hormones balanced and she felt better.

But as sometimes happens when people feel better, Monica did not schedule a follow-up with me. Instead, she just popped in now and again to pick up her progesterone cream. Each time she would report that all was fine, and would occasionally mention that she had developed some joint pain and fatigue.

This routine continued for almost two years, when she finally decided to schedule a follow-up appointment.

Monica reported that she had just gotten back from a famous and renowned health facility on the West Coast. And even though she had no health insurance, and despite the fact that they had fallen on financial hardship, Monica forked out several thousand dollars for a consultation with a specialist, and several thousands more for an MRI and other hi-tech diagnostics. I asked her what their diagnoses was after this full evaluation and the barrage of tests. Embarrassed, she remarked they still did not know what was going on. They wrote her a prescription for prednisone, a potent immune-suppressing medicine. That was it. They told her further tests would need to be done. But Monica was running out of time, literally.

Her eyes were drooping and her life force was almost nil. She had no appetite whatsoever and had dropped over thirty pounds in the previous six months. She appeared undernourished and dehydrated and could barely walk or talk. She was desperate. And frankly, I was concerned for her life.

I did my usual workup. Her immune system was in hyper drive, and she checked for a high viral load, and several other significant organ imbalances. I immediately started her on a whey protein shake supplement and a high protein diet. I insisted that she increase her fluid intake to three times her current intake. I also started her on several immune balancing supplements, including fish oil.

Over the next few sessions I added several other natural medicines to bolster her liver function, and to deal with the chronically high viral load she was carrying. Monica's "undiagnosed" autoimmune symptoms began to subside, and her weight and her energy returned to normal. Within three months Monica was back to her old self, again. She was hot flash-free and feeling a new zest for life.

The high tech, high cost system didn't work for Monica. The allopathic doctors did what they knew how to do. In this case, it wasn't enough. However, a simple yet thorough holistic examination *was* enough to snatch Monica from the jaws of death.

WHAT ARE WE MEASURING, AND WHY?

As a holistic practitioner, this is an area of great frustration for me, and one that I spend a great deal of time and effort working to correct. It's not easy to make the huge cogwheels of the traditional medical system budge. It's even more challenging to get healthcare consumers, even ultra-sensitives, to open their eyes to all their available options for healing. That's because healthcare consumers everywhere have been programmed to believe there is only one set of rules when it comes to diagnosing and measuring health imbalances. I'm sorry. Nothing could be further from the truth.

Fortunately, a grand activation is in process and many ultra-sensitives are awakening to the notion that there are other ways, perhaps better ways, for people to get well and stay well. And it all starts by questioning *what* traditional healthcare practitioners are measuring and evaluating, and why.

AM I IN RANGE?

Mainstream medicine has developed a set of rules over the years, which dictates what types of tests are to be used in the diagnosis and treatment of illness. Whether it's a blood test for the thyroid, liver, cholesterol, or any other bodily function, the standard range for "normal" has been predetermined to meet the needs of the general population worldwide.

There are several issues to consider here. First, ultra-sensitives are not the general population. What's "normal" for others is not necessarily normal for the ultra-sensitive. What may seem to be an "abnormal" result for others may be perfectly normal for an ultra-sensitive. Why? Because our chemistry is different, our neurological wiring is different, we are just plain different.

That's not to say that you should ignore abnormal blood tests or other allopathic test results, but rather to suggest that perhaps normal and abnormal ranges should not be applied so rigorously to everyone. We're not all the same. Not everybody fits into the universal "normal."

GOOD VIBRATIONS

Second, given the unique energetic makeup of the ultra-sensitive, it would make sense that organ health and overall vitality or life force might be better determined by evaluating the *energy level*, or *vibration,* of each organ. In fact, there is a whole new science emerging that is exploring just exactly that.

Finally, one has to ask: Who decided that the things we're actually measuring with today's modern lab tests are even relevant to the issues at hand?

Why are we measuring TSH (thyroid stimulating hormone) levels to determine thyroid functionality when in so many cases those tests produce false negatives and false positives? Why are we so obsessed with measuring total cholesterol levels, when we could be measuring the energy stress to the liver, which is ultimately responsible for cholesterol production? Why is it that liver blood tests are often "normal" when energetic liver congestion actually exists and is contributing to depression, anxiety, indigestion, and much more? Why is it that blood tests and sonograms of the gallbladder often reveal no abnormalities when in fact the gallbladder is inflamed and loaded with gallstones that can't be visualized?

These are just a few of the issues that need to be addressed if we're going to make mainstream healthcare useful, not just to the sensitive, but to the rest of the population. One can only hope that these new methods of diagnosis will one day become headlines in mainstream medicine.

BLOOD TESTS VERSUS KINESIOLOGY

Over the years it has been drilled into the minds of healthcare consumers that blood tests are the only accurate way to measure organ function, hormone levels, blood counts, you name it. I'm sorry. That's just not so. As a holistic practitioner and medical intuitive, I can tell you that helping people overcome this unfounded and antiquated notion has been an area of significant frustration for me.

Why? Determining blood levels does not necessarily tell you what's happening in a particular organ or gland, and it does not take into account imbalances in other organs and systems, which, by the way, are all connected.

A blood test is merely a snap-shot of what's going on only in the bloodstream at that moment, and fails to adequately evaluate what may be going on in other organs and other areas of the body. Blood tests simply do not always provide a complete picture of what's going on within the body.

Unfortunately, people have been led to believe that blood tests are the mandatory "be all, end all" when it comes to diagnosing health imbalances. The truth is, applied kinesiology (AK), or energy testing, may be a far better option for the ultra-sensitive, and for others. It is typically more accurate, is completely non-invasive and offers immediate results, whereas blood tests might have taken weeks or months to schedule, and more days or weeks to get results. Not to mention the significant costs savings AK provides. Then there's always the fear factor. Who wants to get stuck by a needle if that can be avoided?

IT'S ALL ABOUT YOU

AK is a more accurate measurement for ultra-sensitives and others because the practitioner is checking results against *your unique energy field*, your aura, and is not comparing against some standard, pre-determined scale. Results are measured against your specific scale. It measures results based on what's going on in *you.* Therefore results are not just more accurate, they are more relevant.

Because AK is not recognized by the American Medical Association, or by most of its constituents, most people believe it carries no merit. Yet quite the opposite is true. Nowhere is this contrast more confounding than with thyroid hormone and function tests.

DOLORES

Dolores came to my office a bit skeptical. She had been to many allopathic practitioners over the many years, and each had promised to cure her long standing issues with anxiety and insomnia.

Dolores told me she had been taking the thyroid hormone levothyroxine, known by the brand name Synthroid, for over twenty years for the "fatigue" and "low thyroid function" that started in her twenties. Over the years her doctors had been adjusting her doses, and she was still taking a moderate dose of levothyroxine when I met her.

When we visited in my office for the first time, I could sense her skepticism. After all, she'd engaged many practitioners over the years, each unsuccessful in reducing her symptoms. And during that time she'd had every known medical test performed on her, only to have everything come back "normal." I found that quite surprising, since one glance at Dolores and I could tell her thyroid was revving hot.

She handed me her lab reports. Her TSH (thyroid stimulating hormone; a test that screens for thyroid function) was in normal range. Her allopathic doctors were satisfied. I wasn't. Something didn't jive.

I checked her thyroid and her progesterone levels my way, through applied kinesiology. Sure enough, the answers became clear. Dolores' thyroid function was *not* normal. Her thyroid function was actually high, and had probably been running high for much of the time she had been taking her levothyroxine prescription. Dolores was *hyper*thyroid. She was hyperthyroid because she was taking levothyroxine, a medicine that stimulates thyroid function. And it was her hyperthyroid state that was responsible for her chronic low-level anxiety and her insomnia.

I suggested that she taper off her thyroid prescription slowly, with her prescriber's knowledge. I also had Dolores supplement with some progesterone cream to deal with her low progesterone levels. It was her low progesterone level, from an early age on, that was the original cause of her low thyroid function and low energy levels, and this had never been corrected.

At the end of six weeks Dolores called me to report that her anxiety had subsided and her energy levels remained strong, despite being off of her thyroid medicine. She felt so much better that she resumed her favorite pastime, oil painting. Yes, Dolores had become a picture of health.

SENSITIVITY TO MEDICATIONS

Ultra-sensitives are sensitive to medicines, and typically more so than their less-sensitive counterparts. That pretty much says it all. That includes prescription drugs, vitamins, herbs, supplements, and anything else with therapeutic properties, including live juices and protein shakes.

The reality is that many ultra-sensitives need few supplements or none at all, since their bodies will often balance themselves on their own when provided with the proper nutrients. And therein lies the paradox. Too many ultra-sensitives don't pay enough attention to their diet and nutritional status, which ultimately leads to many of the common ultra-sensitive maladies discussed throughout this book. Yes, eating right is paramount to the health and vitality of the ultra-sensitive, and anyone else.

SENSITIVE SUPPLEMENTATION

While ultra-sensitives embark on balancing their health and nutritional status, there may come a time when taking supplements may be appropriate. But sensitive buyers beware. When ultra-sensitives do need prescriptions or supplements, they should be taken in smaller doses, often *one-half to one quarter the usual dose*, and they should be used only when absolutely needed. Otherwise the unsuspecting ultra-sensitive may eventually feel worse rather than better.

The irony is that ultra-sensitives as a whole take more supplements per capita than less-sensitives. Those who visit my office often arrive with shopping bags loaded with supplements. I've had a number of people roll in two suitcases full! These people are taking as many as fifty different products at one time, leaving them almost no time or money for food and nutrition and the rest of their daily living.

One thing is certain. People who take too many supplements, or take too much of a given supplement, can unwittingly cause their own demise. And unfortunately the ultra-sensitive can accomplish this more quickly and easily than others.

BETTY BOOPED

Betty was an easygoing sixty-something woman. A charming woman with an appetite for reading (and believing) everything she read, especially when it came to taking supplements. She loved all the latest and greatest claims about this vitamin, that herb, and everything in between.

All was going well in Betty's life. She felt great on her supplement regimen, for a while. She was taking no less than forty--that's right--*forty* different supplements, most of which she did not need. You see, Betty was an ultra-sensitive. Her self-regulating body really required little to nothing when it came to supplements. She didn't realize what that meant at the time. But when she ended up in my office, looking pale and yellow, with nausea and vomiting, I think she got the message.

Betty had overloaded her body, and especially her liver, with vitamins and herbs. Her liver couldn't eliminate the amount of supplements she was consuming and was beginning to shut down. I instructed her to stop all supplements immediately and begin to drink large amounts of distilled water. I also told her that if her vomiting did not subside in twenty-four hours she was to head to the emergency room for treatment.

Fortunately, we nipped Betty's supplement habit in the bud. She phoned me two weeks later feeling markedly better. Her jaundice had cleared and the vomiting had ceased. I took the opportunity to remind Betty that her supplement cravings also needed to cease. I also reminded her that she was an ultra-sensitive, a powerful self-healer, someone who could easily OD on supplementation. She finally understood.

These days Betty still has hankerings to try new supplements now and again, but fortunately her willpower, and her family support, have taken the upper hand. Today, she uses only a protein shake and a B complex, and feels better than ever.

THE DOCTORS OF THE GOLDEN AGE

So what's an ultra-sensitive to do when health issues arise? How do ultra-sensitives rebalance and recharge themselves when their sensitive immune system and other organs become imbalanced or clogged and overwhelmed by planetary toxins? Can anybody really understand and correct the imbalances in the ultra-sensitive body? Does anybody really understand how the ultra-sensitive body operates?

Yes. We are out there. (And many non-believers think we really are "out there.") We are the medical intuitives who can sense and see organ and energy imbalances and nutritional imbalances, and who can spot emotional blocks and past traumatic events. We are the energy workers who can clear and redirect those blocked energy channels. We go by various titles: Reiki practitioners, acupuncturists, intuitive therapists, and many others. Some of us work with machines that can detect energy and nutritional imbalances; others use our own internal machines. No matter how we accomplish our work, no matter what esoteric shingle we may hang out, if any at all, we are out there, and available to help.

DOC, IS THAT YOU?

It's important to understand that many of the doctors of the traditional healthcare system are themselves ultra-sensitives, even if they don't yet know it and even if they don't know what that means. Many are having a difficult time working within their structured medical paradigm and are ready to evolve to the next level. You can help them with the process. Tell them about the Golden Age doctors who are helping you. Tell them about the new modalities and natural medicines that are working for you. Don't be afraid. They need to know, not just for their good but for yours.

YOU ARE THE HEALER

Ultra-sensitives tend to be powerful healers. It's a part of who we are. We may choose to formalize this gift, hone the skills and market ourselves as such, or we may just choose to heal others through more informal means. Whether or not we choose to develop that gift is a personal decision. The fact remains you are a healer.

Then there are those ultra-sensitive who are not just healers; they are *spontaneous healers*.

What is a spontaneous healer? Spontaneous healers are those who are able to heal *themselves* using only their own energy and their own internal means. Spontaneous healers are often able to resolve their own health imbalances through energy manipulation and nutritional adjustments. For some spontaneous healers this happens continuously and automatically through their subconscious, for others it's accomplished consciously through the power of thought and intent.

No matter how it's accomplished, the concept of spontaneous healing may seem far-fetched for those who have not experienced it first hand. That's understandable given our traditional societal rearing. But having worked with many of these fortunate souls, including myself, I can assure you that spontaneous healing is not only possible and real, but within the reach of many who choose to develop it.

Are you a spontaneous healer?

Signs of a spontaneous healer:

- Symptoms appear quickly, peak, and then just as quickly disappear.
- Through your life you seem to have experienced almost every symptom imaginable (and some that aren't), and most, if not all, eventually go away.
- You are unable to tolerate many supplements and/or don't need them to feel better.
- You have a sense about the cause of your own symptoms and imbalances.
- Healing others comes easily to you.

S.O.S.

We all want to resolve our physical and emotional imbalances and the symptoms they create. Maintaining optimum and vibrant health is important to everyone, but for the ultra-sensitive, it's not only important, it's mandatory. That's because if these symptoms and their source are not cleared, powerful and deep-seated blocks can set in. And these blocks can quickly and efficiently derail the ultra-sensitive from their intended life path. And we don't need that.

So whether you're a practicing healer, a spontaneous healer, or just a delicate ultra-sensitive in distress, if you have symptoms you can't overcome on your own, don't be afraid to ask for help. Seek out a qualified practitioner. Just remember, ultra-sensitives need ultra sensitive healthcare. Just know that it's out there and available, when you need it.

8.

Poverty Pledge

Over my thirty-plus years interacting with ultra-sensitives, the issue of "poverty consciousness" has been one of the most glaring and most frustrating for me to observe. And it still remains one of the most curious and universal paradoxes among ultra-sensitives.

What exactly do I mean by "poverty consciousness?" I mean that many ultra-sensitives are wired to believe that they don't deserve to be abundant and successful. Yet nothing could be further from the truth. Given the nature of our work on this planet, ultra-sensitives deserve abundance and success as much as anybody else, if not more.

Yet, somehow, healers, light workers, readers, channels, and the like seem to believe, either consciously or subconsciously, that they don't deserve to receive payment for services rendered. Or they may feel that the services they render aren't worthy of reasonable compensation. Why that is remains a mystery, although there appear to be some karmic, past-life influences at play. Whatever the reason, believing that you and your services are not worthy is just not okay. This is not just a minor issue. It's a pandemic.

Many ultra-sensitives feel as though it's their planetary "duty" to be completely selfless, to give from the heart without expecting anything in return. While these noble qualities may have been appropriate while we existed in other dimensions or on other planets far, far away, they do NOT hold true while in body on Planet Earth doing the work we came here to do.

IT'S DIFFERENT NOW

Things are different in this realm, here on Planet Earth. We live in a different matrix now, one that requires us to eat, to sleep, to keep our now physical body sheltered, to provide the daily pleasures that keep us vital and happy. And on this planet at this time, that requires resources, energy…money. And it's not only our right to have the money we need to accomplish these things, it's a necessity.

WHERE'S THE MONEY?

Money is energy. And as ultra-sensitives, we're all about energy. We ARE energy. When you provide a product or service you deserve to be compensated for that energy exchange. If you give out a lot of energy you deserve to receive an equivalent amount of energy in return. In this society, at least for the time being, that energy is money. It's yours and you deserve it.

The time is now for ultra-sensitives everywhere to clear the old cellular memories with regard to abundance and self worth. We came here to do great things, to do powerful things, and we deserve the recognition and abundance that comes along with it. With that in mind:

There's something you need to acknowledge and accept right now:

You are brilliant!

Can you handle that? It's time you did, so get used to it.

You are gifted, intuitive, and great at what you do. You're good at so many things some would say you might have "natural ADD." That's a good thing. In fact, at times as an ultra-sensitive, you are so overwhelmed by how much you know, you can barely comprehend how good you are. In short, you are brilliant. Accept it.

IT'S OKAY TO BE BRILLIANT

We came here to be brilliant. We came here to succeed in all that we do. It's okay to be great. So stop worrying about how people will judge you for being that good. And trust me. You're that good. You're better than you could have imagined. And if you find yourself starting to worry about what others might think about you and your wild success, remember this:

What others think about you is none of your business.

Just do what you came here to do and do it brilliantly!

Try this simple exercise:

Say this to yourself: **I am brilliant.** Go ahead. Don't be shy. Try it. Take a few seconds to try it. I'll wait. Go in front of a mirror and look at yourself and say aloud: "I am brilliant."

Feels uncomfortable at first, doesn't it? Try it again. This time allow yourself to mean it, and more importantly, accept it. Go ahead. Take thirty seconds or so and say it again, aloud, in front of the mirror. After you speak the words, take a moment to see how it fits you.

Practice this exercise at least once before you begin your routine each day. If during the day you find yourself doubting yourself, or if you start feeling inadequate (and ultra-sensitives tend to do this more than most) repeat this exercise. In fact, repeat it as often as you need to, dozens of times per day if necessary.

SELF-SABOTAGE

It's true that some ultra-sensitives feel they are physically or emotionally unable to bring their energies into the traditional workplace, or choose not to for other reasons. I honor those personal and necessary choices. Still, others *do* choose to bring their gifts to the world and they work hard for the money (thank you, Donna Summer).Very hard. They desperately do want to achieve financial abundance, yet at the end of the day it seems they just can't get it done. For some peculiar reason it seems that when these motivated souls are just on the verge of a big break, everything seems to fall apart at the eleventh hour, just dissipate into the ethers. Why is that?

Simply, we do it to ourselves. It seems a part of our subconscious mind has been genetically coded to avert success. This coding seems to override any and all of our diligent and conscious efforts to get it done, to get to home plate. I call it the ultra-sensitive sabotage.

Features of the ultra-sensitive sabotage:

Many ultra-sensitives…

- Don't believe they could really be that good.
- Suffer from one of the physical or emotional maladies that tend to plague this group of individuals, such as chronic fatigue syndrome, depression, or another auto-immune disorder, ADHD/ADD, (see corresponding chapters in Part Two) making it difficult for them to become motivated to do anything at all, even unable to hold down a regular job.
- Don't have a plan on how to best utilize their skills and abilities
- Believe that others may perceive them as conceited and aloof if they were to be successful.
- Believe they are too weak or too meek to handle success.
- Do not want to be in the limelight, and are truly attention-phobic.
- Are fearful that they are too sensitive to interact with the public at any level.
- Seem satisfied just eeking out enough money to feed and house themselves. Worse yet, a good many ultra-sensitives are literally on the verge of living in poverty.
- Seem to have genetic lineage and past life karma connections that would have them believe they don't deserve to be abundant and successful.
- Believe that they lack the resources, financial and otherwise to be successful.
- Feel guilty about taking money from others.

Want to break the cycle? Do you want to have the opportunity to be as successful as possible? You can do this. You can overcome this antiquated genetic coding, the ultra-sensitive sabotage, just by realizing and acknowledging that it exists and that it has control over you. That's it. It's that simple. Start today.

Know you are successful.
Think as though you are already successful,
and you will become successful.

Start living that credo every day and you will be successful. And do remember that success will be awarded to you in the way that's perfect for you and your soul path. It will be yours for the asking.

THE BACKUP PLAN

There's yet another reason why many ultra-sensitives (and less-sensitives) seem to never quite thrive financially: They have a backup plan. That's right. They *have* a backup plan: It's called poverty. And from this side of the page, that's just unacceptable.

If you have a backup plan, there is an unconscious tendency to never give quite enough attention and energy to the original plan, Plan A. That's because in the back of your mind you've allowed yourself to have another option waiting and available, Plan B. With a backup plan we subconsciously leave the door open for failure. And you can guess what happens then.

Forget the backup plan. Instead, stay focused and true to who you really are; the authentic you, and what you want to accomplish in this life. Don't fill your plate with dozens of options. Focus on using the skills and interests that light your fire, the ones that can truly help you fulfill your life's passion.

Want to be successful? Dust off the attribute that best defines *you*, whatever that may be--healing, writing, singing, channeling, painting--and stay true to it. Fill yourself with the inspiration, the butterflies, and the excitement that comes with finding your true calling. Then start putting these skills to good use, today and every day, and you will be fulfilled.

MANIFEST IT

Remember that as ultra-sensitives we are powerful manifesters. So do think and act carefully. Make sure you know what you want, because you're likely to get it. That means making a plan. It doesn't have to be a fancy or elaborate plan. Just put your plan in writing. Even on a napkin will do. That will force you to organize your thoughts and create the intent necessary to bring your plan to fruition.

You want a successful business or occupation? Manifest it. You want a thriving private practice as an energy worker? Manifest it. Want to create abundance? *Manifest it.* And even though you don't necessarily need lots of money to manifest your plan, it doesn't hurt to have it. Should you strive to make some? Yes. But don't let the lack of money keep you from making a plan to get started. Make a plan. Make it today.

DON'T GIVE UP NOW!

Has your life been a story of one failure after another? Do you feel like you'll never find the success? Have you tried and tried for so long that you're too tired to try again? Don't give up now. It may just be that the timing for your success wasn't quite right yet. It took one-hundred door-to-door solicitation calls for Colonel Saunders to find a buyer for his secret recipe of herbs and spices. It took Mr. Hershey six colossal business failures before he hit onto his sweet success. Your time will come, too.

So don't let past failures keep you from the overwhelming successes that await you. Success is out there, and when it's time, it will make a grand appearance. And you deserve it.

GINA

Gina, a gentle, lovely lady in her early fifties, was referred to me because she was stuck in her career and in her ability to nourish herself. When it came to business, she couldn't seem to catch a lucky break no matter what she tried. When I met Gina she was barely able to walk into my office without becoming physically exhausted. She had been selling her paintings and her hand-made jewelry just to make ends meet. But lately she didn't have the energy to even do that.

When we first visited, she asked me point blank, "Why is my life such a disaster?" She went on to explain that every time she thought she'd found a buyer for one of her paintings the deal fell through. She also confessed that she felt guilty accepting the money from people who wanted to buy her work. She went on to explain that her life had been one "almost made it" experience after another. Gina was clearly despondent over her life journey so far.

Gina had tried so hard to make things happen over the years that she began to neglect her health and nutrition. When I checked her blood sugars, she was hypoglycemic, craving mostly sweets and not much more. More than that, her iron levels were very low and she was clearly dehydrated. Her liver had become clogged with angst and frustration, so much so that her facial skin took on that classic liver-yellow tinge. Gina had become malnourished to the point that her organs were beginning to fail. She needed nutritional balancing immediately.

I started her on a whey protein shake twice daily, along with supplemental protein loads. We restored her iron stores with sublingual vitamin B12 and iron. I also added a milk thistle complex for liver support. I instructed Gina to eat no less than five small meals daily, each with protein in it. She happily complied. She began to eat more beef and chicken, and started drinking the half gallon of distilled water I instructed her to consume daily. Her life force began to awaken.

In our following sessions we discussed the issue of money in exchange for services. Gina worked meticulously to create exquisite jewelry pieces to sell. I made sure she understood the value of her time and the value of the beautiful pieces she created.

Then I told her what she desperately needed to know. I told her she was brilliant. I told her that her work was brilliant. I did this not to appease, but because I meant it. At first she blushed shyly. I told her again. This time she knew I was serious. It took a few explanations, but Gina finally got it. And she began to live it.

Within two weeks Gina's mood and vitality perked up. She was alive again! Over the next few months Gina resumed her jewelry making work and had regained the energy and inspiration to start doing her jewelry trade shows. The money started to come in, and Gina was elated to be on her path once again.

EAT RICH

Now I'm not talking about eating Crème Brule everyday (although you can). I am suggesting, however, that you make sure to nourish yourself properly every day, so that you have the energy and vitality to be as successful as possible.

Sounds like a simple assignment, yet the majority of ultra-sensitives that I have worked with fail miserably at it. Most are poorly nourished. Most are protein deficient. Most don't consume enough calories to replenish the tremendous amounts of energy they expend every day just by being who they are. If you lack the zip, the motivation, the inspiration to get out of the poverty rut, whether it's physical or emotional energy you lack, start by correcting your diet.

Eat for success. Choose a healthy, clean diet. It doesn't have to be vegan or vegetarian, just a balanced and complete meal consumed three to six times daily. Consume high quality protein in each of your meals. Don't skip meals and do drink plenty of purified water.

If you need help getting your nutrition right, seek the services of a qualified holistic practitioner to develop your personal diet plan.

MAKE IT HAPPEN!

Are you ready to accomplish all the things you came here to do? Are you ready to be as successful as you've always imagined? Are you ready to shed the jinx of the poverty consciousness?

Take the abundance pledge:

- From this moment on, I will be gracious and grateful when it comes to earning and accepting money. It's an even energy exchange. I put out my energy; and in return I receive energy back in the form of money.
- I deserve abundance. My life is free of financial struggle.
- I will graciously accept money and opportunities to make money. It is the universe's gift to me.

- I will allow myself to provide my products and services free of charge only when that is what is in my heart, but that will be the exception rather than the rule.
- I may also accept products and services as an even exchange for my energy expenditure. (This bartering system will become more commonplace over the next few years, especially among ultra-sensitives.)

Feel free to repeat this pledge whenever you find yourself doubting your worth, and as often as you need to. The more often you recite it and believe the words you read the more quickly it will come to pass. Make it part of your daily routine and succeed!

Yes, you may be an ultra-sensitive, but you're an ultra-sensitive on Planet Earth. Abundance is your birthright. Accept it and enjoy it. You deserve it.

9.

The Intuitive Sensitive

Everyone is born with the gift of intuition. Yet so many people don't realize what it is, or that it's even available to them. You too may not yet have developed or trusted your intuition fully, but it's in there. And it's waiting to be awakened. You may choose to accept the gift of intuition and use it, or you may choose to ignore the gift and go on about your life, making decisions in a different way. That's the beauty of life. We get to choose.

Over the years I've encountered hundreds of ultra-sensitives who didn't realize that they had intuitive gifts. I've also met some who did recognize their gift but chose to ignore it for various reasons. That's okay. Neither choice is wrong. There are no wrong choices in life, only different kinds of lessons. But do keep this in mind. As an ultra-sensitive, you've been gifted with the opportunity to do great things in this life. So why not make the most of the tools you've been given?

YOU ARE A RECEIVER. TUNE IN

Discovering and using your intuition is not as difficult, and certainly not as "mysterious" as many believe. You simply have to pay attention to what you're feeling, to what you're feeling about everything and everyone around you. That's it.

Just remember that you are a sensitive. You feel everything. Start paying close attention to *what* you're feeling. Then just keep fine tuning your internal receiver until it gives you the information you're looking for, and you'll be well on your way to developing your intuitive skills. If you're ready to start developing your intuition to its fullest potential, work that muscle, every day. Many ultra-sensitives already do, and don't even realize that they're doing it.

For instance, you think about someone, and they call you on the phone or show up in your life moments later. You find a parking place because you just visualized it in your mind's eye. Sometimes it's something simple like choosing that menu item that's just what you were craving. As ultra-sensitives, we use our intuition unconsciously to make dozens of decisions each day, mostly without realizing it.

Why did you choose to buy this book? You had a hunch, a sense, a "feeling." You just knew. You knew that there was something in here you needed to read; something that would help you along your life path. That's your intuition at work. It's an amazing and wondrous gift.

USE IT OR LOSE IT

Cliché? You bet. True? You bet. It's the crux of an important theorem that ultra-sensitives, and less-sensitives alike will benefit from understanding. And it's a universal truth that applies to so many things in life:

If you ignore something long enough, it will eventually go away.

This holds true for your intuitive gifts as well, with this caveat. If you are supposed to develop and use your intuitive faculties in this lifetime, *and you do not*, the universe will let you know, one way or another. It's called intuitive stifling. If you stifle your intuition long enough, you'll likely begin to experience some uncomfortable physical and emotional symptoms.

As always, the first few signs may be subtle and gentle. But over time, if you are contracted to use your gifts in this lifetime as a healer, an intuitive, an energy worker, or the like, these symptoms will become unmistakable, even intolerable.

Make no mistake. Ultra-sensitives who stifle their gifts of intuition can go on to develop a host of uncomfortable physical and emotional symptoms. Here is a list of just a few that may already be plaguing you:

Symptoms of a stifled intuition:

- Headaches

- Depression
- Anxiety or Panic Attacks
- Night terrors
- Visual problems
- Heart disease
- Hearing loss
- Insomnia
- Blood sugar imbalances; hyper or hypo
- ADHD symptoms
- Bipolar symptoms
- Schizophrenia

GEORGE'S JOURNEY

George was a gentle man: soft-spoken, yet strong, inquisitive, yet naive. When I met him he was suffering from severe bouts of depression and insomnia and chronic low-level anxiety and panic attacks, which he'd had most all of his life. No prescription medicines had resolved these symptoms. He had tried them all over the years. Xanax, Valium, Prozac, Wellbutrin, you name it. George had tried them, without success.

Things had reached a crisis. He got to the point where he could not hold down a job; he could barely leave his house. All he was able to manage was an electronic connection with the world, through his computer. He literally spent all his time living life through the Internet.

When we first visited by phone, George confessed that he was contemplating suicide. This was an emergency. He knew it, and I felt it. I conducted my usual interview and history with him. But it didn't take long to find the source of the symptoms.

You see, George was the black sheep of the family. He had had a very traditional upbringing. He went on to describe how he had lived in a "fairy world" since he was old enough to remember. He saw elves and fairies, even angels who would swoop down now and again to play with him. He had been able to see these beings and, as an adult, still did from time to time.

George recalled, at age six, telling his mother about these sightings--but only once. His mother told his father, who assured him there were no such things as fairies and such. His father accused him of making up these stories, called it a vivid imagination, or a bad dream. They had even contemplated taking him in for a psychiatric evaluation. That was all it took.

For the following twenty years George tried to "shoo" his unseen friends away. But it didn't matter. The sightings increased over time. Not only that, George began to see and feel energies and beings in his bedroom, and around the auras of other people. He was beside himself, torn between needing to get clarity and verification of his sanity, and making sense of it within the context of what society said was real. The tug of war ensued, until our regression session together.

George lived five hundred miles from my office. He needed to be energetically opened immediately. Traveling to my office was not an option. So we did it by phone.

A state of light hypnosis did the trick. We were able to reveal a past life where George practiced as a wizard. And a wonderful wizard he was. He dealt with alchemy and communicated with the elemental world, with the fairies and the nature spirits, and the like. The session was so profound, his outpouring of emotions so strong, I had to carefully taper the session to a close. It was as though we had opened the floodgates. But a flood was what we needed. This outpouring triggered the activation I was looking for.

After several weeks of memory integration from this past life, George began to calm. He began to sleep. His mood began to lift, although we did supplement with some SAM-e and inositol through the transition period.

Within six months, George was a different person. He was still able to visit with his unseen family and friends, but this time he was doing something with it. He began to hold seminars where he taught others how to activate *their* intuitive callings. His parents never really understood what was going on, but eventually their ridicule turned into smiles and respect for their son's gifts.

George had the gift, and he finally used it. And today this realm and others are a better place because of it.

ACKNOWLEDGE IT

So ask yourself, what gifts are *you* holding inside of you? Are you the psychic medium? Are you the energy worker? Perhaps you're the interplanetary communicator, or the insightful animal communicator. Perhaps there's another unique calling that's been carefully tucked away inside you, that's been waiting to become activated at just the right moment.

It matters not what you do with your gifts, *as long as you do something with them*, something positive that's of benefit to yourself and to others. Because whenever the ultra-sensitive does something to benefit their own wellbeing, they are ultimately doing something to improve the wellbeing of all. At the end of the day, that's what ultra-sensitives are programmed to do. We're here to balance the planet, its inhabitants, and beyond.

One thing is for sure. Ultra-sensitives have powerful intuition. It's a pivotal part of our makeup. Use yours to choose what you want to do. Then trust that the decision you make is perfect for you. Just trust.

10.

Hibernation Override Syndrome

We all know that bears and other animals hibernate during the winter season. But did you know that humans are supposed to hibernate, too? That's right. We are. Especially ultra-sensitives. And when we don't, our bodies and minds will find a way to let us know that we should.

Yes, as a species we are supposed to hibernate during the winter months, just like many other mammals. But instead, we keep pushing. We keep working. We keep the same long hours we always keep. We push ourselves, physically and emotionally, through the winter months, and it often feels as though we're forcing something that shouldn't be forced. It seems as though we're trying to make our bodies and minds do something they don't want to do, and really weren't designed to do. The result? What I call Hibernation Override Syndrome, HOS.

HOS is a group of symptoms that have been overlooked during our lifetime, and really through the entire industrial age, as a result of pushing our sensitive bodies in ways they should not be pushed. These symptoms seem to occur most often between mid-October to mid-February, sometimes longer, depending on what part of the world you reside in.

Have you ever experienced Hibernation Override Syndrome during your winter season?

Symptoms of Hibernation Override Syndrome (HOS):

- Depression and moodiness
- Excessive fatigue and grogginess

- Anger and edginess
- Body aches and pains
- Lightheadedness
- Restless sleep
- Spatial disorientation
- Foggy headedness
- Sadness
- Reminiscence
- Confusion
- Headaches
- Decreased visual acuity
- Increased hunger and thirst
- Feeling like you need to cry
- Difficulty speaking
- Difficulty concentrating

What's happening to you during *your* hibernation?

MOODY BLUES

It's no secret that people tend to become more depressed, sad, even extra agitated and edgy during the winter months. In fact, this is a well-documented occurrence across the globe. And as usual, ultra-sensitives tend to feel these symptoms more than most. Popular thinking would have you believe that shorter days or the winter weather is to blame. There is some of that. What's also at play is a change in our overall emotional state. Our minds want to turn down for the winter. They want to rest and rejuvenate and stay clear of left-brain logical thinking. They're certainly not prepared to handle the high levels of stress that we create during the hibernation season. The result is often those "moody blues," mood changes that seem to defy any type of intervention.

To make matters worse, ultra-sensitives are powerful empaths. We feel everything. In many cases, we are feeling and taking on the mood changes, anxiety, stress, and sadness of others during this season, including not only those you closely interact with on a daily basis but those you may have never even met, halfway across the globe. In fact, in many cases you're feeling the cumulative angst of the entire planet without even realizing it. And that's a huge burden for any individual, a burden that can send even the most stout ultra-sensitive into the blues.

WINTER SLEEPIES

Feeling a bit sleepy through the winter months? Welcome to hibernation season. This is a common malady for most everybody during the winter season. We seem to tire more quickly during the winter months, and feeling extra sleepy during the waking hours is a common occurrence for many. Many ultra-sensitives can't wait for the sun to go down, so they can justify their early bedtime. We're craving sleep 24/7, and that's normal. That's because we're supposed to be resting. When we ignore that calling, ultra-sensitives, like others, will find themselves feeling far less alert, more foggy headed, and even disoriented during the daytime hours of hibernation season.

DEPERSONALIZATION

The symptoms of HOS can bring about some unusual sensations in the ultra-sensitive. One worth mentioning is what I refer to as the syndrome of "de-personalization." Depersonalization is a full body sensation that literally feels like you are not really in your body, and it can be a bit disconcerting, even frightening. It's a syndrome of sensations that occur because your soul wants to leave, and to some extent actually does leave for a while to get some well-deserved rest.

The symptoms of depersonalization include feelings of extreme apprehension, edginess, and disorientation, even paranoia. Appetite changes with feelings of nausea can also ensue. These episodes can last from a few minutes to a few hours at a time, even up to several days. Some ultra-sensitives even say they feel this way all year round, and learn to adapt to it.

In my experience there is no danger in experiencing these unusual feelings, and, in fact, it may well be that this sensation is a symptom of your soul's evolution; a sign that you are in a rapid mode of activation of your ultra-sensitive sense. So honor the sensation and give your body a break. Give it the rest it needs, especially during hibernation season.

Feeling sleepy? Go ahead. Grab your Teddy and take a nap. Get some rest. It's what your sensitive body needs.

FOOD FOR THOUGHT

We've all experienced this before. Winter months are upon us and suddenly, the days get shorter, the nights get longer and colder. Then, like clockwork our appetites seem to increase. Many of us even put on a few pounds, some more than a few. It's just another sign that the season is upon you. Follow your instincts. If you're hungry, eat. Just choose the right foods. In general that means eating lean meat protein and plenty of complex carbohydrates like whole grains and vegetables. Stay clear of processed foods, fast foods, and unnecessary spices and seasonings, and do try to avoid foods you are allergic to. Easy on caffeine and alcohol, and drink plenty of distilled water. Not sure what foods are right for you? Read my book, *Extreme Clearing for Perfect Health.* There are plenty of diet and nutrition tips throughout.

And don't fret about the winter season weight gain. For most of us it's a natural event, like the bear that gorges himself to prepare for the cold days ahead. And rest assured that your body's thermostat will typically re-adjust itself when spring hits, and the pounds and your appetite will adjust accordingly. Coincidence? No such thing. It's just hibernation season; another one of the cycles of life.

TANYA'S TRIBULATIONS

I met Tanya in my office during the winter of 2006. She walked into the office with laundry list of health problems: Joint pains, mood swings, and overwhelming fatigue. Most intriguing, though, were her complaints of feeling disoriented and spacey over the past few weeks.

Tanya was an office manager for a large organization, where she supervised a dozen well-trained professionals. All was going well until winter hit, when out of nowhere she found herself unable to stay focused in her job. She found it difficult to meet deadlines and handle multiple tasks, like she once could. She was also making errors in judgment, and her bouts of edginess had alienated her boss through increased confrontational interactions, which is what brought her into my office.

I reviewed Tanya's diet and the many supplements she was taking. All was in order, except for one thing. Tanya was an ultra-sensitive and an extreme empath, hence she was being heavily affected by the energies, many negative and unbalanced, of her co-workers. She was adamant to remind me that she had no difficulty handling these pressures during the summer and spring months, but now she felt like she was losing her edge.

She wasn't losing her edge. She was losing her emotional stamina due to Hibernation Override Syndrome. Tanya's job, like many others, continued to be busy all year round. But because of her sensitivity her body and mind just couldn't keep up with the physical and emotional demands this time of year.

I discussed the hibernation concept with her. I also asked her to honor what she was feeling. I told her to quit pushing so hard, especially during the winter months. At first she was flabbergasted at the concept, but then it all started to make sense. She had recalled that she felt this way every holiday season for as long as she could remember.

I started her on extra B vitamins and vitamin C. I also added SAM-e to help maintain her mood and improve her aches and pains. Within several weeks Tanya was in full control, back to her productive self. But the difference was she had lowered her expectations for her personal performance just enough to give her body and mind the rest it was craving.

Now, every holiday season Tanya sends me a little note assuring me that she's "turned down the thermostat" for the season. You can too.

Do you want to honor your natural biorhythms and feel better during the winter months, and all year round?

Follow these steps:

- Get out of your left brain, your logical thinking mind. Start using your creative *right brain.* Paint, sing, dance, write, decorate. Do whatever feels right. Just be extra creative, and don't forget to follow your feelings and hunches--your intuition.
- Take a vacation during the winter months. You're ready. It doesn't have to be Hawaii; it just has to be a getaway. Remember, vacations are not just for the summer season.
- Read a good book, or write a good book. (I prefer the latter.)
- Re-discover your hobbies. Forgot what those are? Think back to when you were age fifteen. What turned you on as a kid? Whatever it is you enjoyed back then is still in you now. You'll find it. It's in there.
- Stay clear of prescription anti-depressants, anti-anxiety, and other mood- or mind-altering drugs as much as possible. They blunt your creativity and your emotions and can actually make matters worse for ultra-sensitives.
- **Emote**. We were all designed to cry. Crying is the single most powerful emotional clearing technique there is. It's free and you can use it anytime you wish. Please do use it, especially you ultra-sensitive men. And there are a lot of you out there.
- Become more social, if it feels right. Connecting with like-minded folks can boost your mood and your inspiration.
- Don't allow negative people to ruin a perfectly good season. Keep the unwanted family visits short and sweet. Hang around people with positive energy, and avoid the rest.
- Stay clear of crowds and crowded places. Protect yourself energetically with your mantras, dark stones, and other divination tools.
- If you need some natural support for mood swings, try using St. John's Wort, 5HTP, or SAM-e as directed, but only one at a time and none in combination with any existing prescription antidepressants. For anxiety, try inositol 500mg to 1000mg up to four times daily, or l-theanine 200mg once to twice daily. These can help get you through the winter doldrums and the angst of the season, should they arise. (See Part II: *How to Manage Mood Swings*)
- Go to bed earlier. Give your body permission to deviate from the summer high- energy routine. Things are different now.

- Sleep no less than seven hours, but try not to exceed nine hours. Too much sleep can cause other issues if continued on a regular basis.
- Your adrenals are trying to rest. Give them a break. Start taking pantothenic acid 500mg twice daily with food. Taking extra vitamin C with the bioflavonoids will also give them a boost.
- Let's not forget drinking plenty of purified water. Shoot for eight to twelve good size glasses per day, but not within two hours of bedtime. Distilled is preferred.
- Make sure your sleeping room is clear of clutter and electronics and properly darkened, and the temperature is suitable. Then, sweet dreams!

TO EVERY SEASON

As ultra-sensitives, we are exquisitely attuned to the natural rhythms of the planet, the stars, and all of the energy cycles of the Universe. Our sensitive bodies, minds, and spirits are designed to follow these cycles. When we artificially force ourselves into routines that are not in alignment with these natural cycles we can create unwanted physical and emotional symptoms. Yes, swimming upstream can be very uncomfortable.

So this time, when winter and the hibernation season rolls around, go with the flow, and avert the complications of Hibernation Override Syndrome. Or make friends with a groundhog. He'll let you know when it's time to pop your head out once again, for the start of a brand new season.

11.

Why Am I Here, Really?

This is the question on the minds of ultra-sensitives everywhere. And guess what? It's time to get the answers. But first, let's examine the problem.

CLOCKWORK

Millions of people across the globe have the same routine. You may be familiar with it. They get up in the morning, get dressed, and rush off to a nine-to-five job. Now that may seem like a simple task for most people, but as an ultra-sensitive, functioning in a nine-to-five routine can be a daunting and painful task. For many ultra-sensitives, the forty-hour-per-week drill can be nothing short of a struggle.

Why a struggle, you ask? Here are a couple of scenarios that may jolt your memory: Does this sound familiar?

- You can't relate to the work you're doing. It seems tedious and meaningless within the scope of the big picture and all that you understand.
- The people you work with are harsh and closed minded, and they treat you like a second-class citizen.
- Lunch break is an uncomfortable social event that you could do without, mostly because it seems like no one sees anything the way you do, and you have little in common and nothing to talk about.
- Your boss doesn't get you, and you can see right through him (or her).
- It takes all the energy and fortitude you can muster just to make it through the day.

Ready for the five o'clock whistle? Who can blame you? After all, you're an ultra-sensitive. And for many ultra-sensitives the nine-to-five routine just doesn't feel right.

So if we're not here to sell shoes at Macy's, or dole out pills in a hospital, or answer phones for the boss, what *are* we here to do? What did you come here to do? More aptly posed, what is our mission on Planet Earth?

IT'S INSIDE YOU

What I have found over many years of observing this quandary is that the answer is carefully tucked away in our cellular memory, in our subconscious. It's been strategically placed; ready to be deciphered by those who are ready and willing to discover it. Unfortunately, many of us go through our entire lives not realizing that it's hiding right there, right under our eyes, ready to be taken and put to good use. Yes, the truth about who we are and what we're here to do lies within.

Sadly, most people, including the ultra-sensitives, will spend a whole lifetime searching for these answers and never find them. Still other ultra-sensitives won't realize that there is even anything to search *for*. Many go on believing that it must be normal to have lost their passions, their purpose, their goals; the things that give their lives meaning or fulfillment. Instead, over time, they come to believe that the nine-to-five must be all they came here to do, simply because nothing else has been presented to them. But an activation is underway, and you are part of it. It's all around you and it's *in you*. Yes, something is stirring. You're beginning to feel an unexplainable hunger, and we're not talking about the enchilada plate.

FEED THE HUNGER

After years of the workplace grind, after years of waiting and wondering, you're beginning to feel a gnawing inside of you; a longing to become something else, to do something else...*anything else*. You're beginning to feel this urgency, a knowing that you came here to do something important, something extraordinary. But you're not sure what that is quite yet. Is that how you're feeling? Well, you're not alone.

Indeed, there is a mass re-awakening occurring across the globe, even as you read these words. It's a global re-awakening, and you and I and many others around us are smack dab in the middle of it right now. Ultra-sensitives everywhere are beginning to sense and embrace who they came here to be. They're discovering their **Marching Orders.** You can, too.

HOW DO I FIND *MY* MARCHING ORDERS?

Start by paying attention to what's going *right* in your life, and what's *not* going right in your life. And start asking poignant questions, the ones most of us tend to shy away from. These are your clues. Here are just a few questions to consider asking yourself. Make sure you answer them truthfully, from your soul space, and not from your personality:

- Is your job making you feel sick or depressed? Or does it inspire you?
- Do your relationships bring you down, or support you?
- Is money controlling your life, or are you controlling your money?
- Have you always wanted to do something else, or are you absolutely content on your life path?
- Are you as creative as you know you can be, or do you feel stifled?

When you take a close look at the answers to these and questions like these, you will begin to get a true sense of why, indeed, you are here. It may take a bit of time for it all to sink in, but the puzzle pieces will eventually fall into place, and you will know.

TAKE A PEEK INSIDE

Next, start trusting your gut feelings, your intuition. Begin to take a closer look at your life and the events that have led you to this very moment by using your "soft vision". This soft vision will allow you to open up to many of the unseen aspects of your life. In fact, take a few moments right now to tune into your sensitive receiver. Let's take a glimpse inside.

Try this simple exercise:

Go ahead. Let your mind run free. Begin to envision yourself completely unencumbered in your life. You have no financial responsibilities, no money worries, no one to report to, you can do whatever you wish (so long as it doesn't interfere with the free will of others)… that's it. Let the feelings and images flow in. What do you see yourself doing? Do you see yourself feeling fulfilled doing that thing? Is this the thing you've always dreamed about doing? Trust what you get. You'll know you're on track when these sensations and images give you butterflies.

Excellent! You've just opened the door to finding out who you really are and what you've come here to do. So don't give up now!

BRING IT FORWARD

Q and A with the soul and intuitive exploration are not the only ways to learn about your marching orders. Many find the answers through past life regression therapy. Regression therapy can open the doors to a remembrance not otherwise accessible to the conscious mind. It can give you powerful insight into who you once were and what your passions once were, and in the process create a present-life activation of the very same skills and abilities. And the results are often quick and profound.

DIANA KNEW

But she hadn't yet remembered when she showed up in my office. Diana was a thirty-six year old mother of two. She reported that she had been suffering from severe migraine headaches for years. These headaches had gotten to the point that they were completely disabling her, physically, emotionally, spiritually, even financially. She had no money left and had difficulty holding down her job as a cafeteria supervisor.

When we first visited, I quickly sensed that her liver was out of balance. And for good reason. Diana had been harboring enormous amounts of anger toward her husband, her children, everyone. She hated her life and nothing was going her way. Not only had her job become a chore, nothing else in her life inspired her. Her pent-up anger had thrown her liver into a tizzy, which in turn resulted in fatigue, depression, digestive problems, and joint aches. Yes, all of her physical and emotional symptoms were related to a single, simple imbalance (as they often are).

After only two sessions together, Diana finally broke down. She admitted that several years back she had wanted to learn how to channel and develop her intuitive gifts. Her mother was also an intuitive and a healer, and had openly worked with these gifts. Diana, on the other hand, had a family to raise and was the primary bread winner. She had never found the time to follow her passion, her marching orders as an intuitive healer. Instead, she had ignored this calling most of her life, stifling her passions and her longings and her joy. We discussed these issues and decided that a regression session was in order.

After a single past-life regression in my office Diana, had learned that her most recent past life was as a Native American shaman. She had been a powerful and important influence in her tribe, and these skills and abilities had passed through to her current life. This was a powerful and unmistakable skill set. Yet Diana had set it aside.

After the session, her tears flowed and flowed. After they dried on her cheeks, Diana quickly perked up. The realization had set in. She was still that shaman. Diana lit up like a firecracker. Her orders had been revealed. For the first time, she saw them clearly, and this infused her with a massive dose of inspiration.

Over the next eight months Diana became a sponge, filling herself with everything spiritual and healing. Not only did her liver come back into balance, her mood lifted and her energy soared. She found a way to balance her job with her passions, and began perform healings for others for a fee. Today she remains symptom free, but most important, she knows what she's here to do, and why. Diana had uncovered her marching orders.

GO WITHIN

Meditation can also help locate your marching orders, and pretty much anything else you've been searching for. But don't let the notion of a structured OM meditation scare you away. Meditation can be accomplished most anytime, and anywhere, and without assuming the lotus position. Yes, you can connect with the higher realms and get answers to your life questions any time of day, even with your eyes wide open. Lots of people do, most without realizing it. I know that I do.

Every morning I take a power walk; thirty minutes of complete mindlessness. I just let my mind go free (except at intersections). It is during this thirty minute ritual that I seem to have the greatest access to new thinking and new ideas. I simply allow my mind to explore the deepest and most distant realms. And I often get there. You can too. Just allow yourself to un-tether your mind, let it go free, then trust that the hunches, feelings, and images you receive are real. Because they are. Did you get a vision? A feeling? Did you stir up some powerful emotions, or get butterflies about that new project idea? If so, you're on the right path.

DO WHAT YOU LOVE

...and you will love what you do. That's the passion bubbling inside you, inside many ultra-sensitives, just waiting to be expressed. Do you love working with PC's? Then your role is to work with technology to help usher in and maintain those machines during the transition. Do you love working with children? Then allow yourself to find a venue where you can teach the next generation what you know. Or perhaps you'll even write a manual or guide for teaching these children.

Perhaps your passion is singing, dancing, or playing a musical instrument (even if you haven't done it since you were a teenager!). Then start doing more of these things and trust that you may be on the verge of uncovering your true marching orders.

Don't worry about how good you are at first. You'll get better at it, because it's your passion. And like many who express their passion in life, you will help heal others in the process. That's right. You can heal others simply through the expression of your passion. Believe this. Amy did.

SING AMY, SING

My daughter Amy was only six years old when I heard her singing along to a song on the car radio. I turned around and looked at her in the back seat, to make sure it was actually her hitting those notes. To my astonishment and delight, she hit every note to the tee. I knew right there and then that singing and music was her calling. So did Amy.

Today, at age twenty-five, Amy sings all over the world. She sings at any venue where she can bring joy and healing to those who listen. She lives for her music, and the truth is, many now live *because* of her music, her amazing voice; her vibrational healing. Healing others with her voice is Amy's marching orders.

SIGN ME UP

Finally, watch for the signs, everywhere. The universe works in amazing and wondrous ways, providing guidance and wisdom in ways that usually defy logic. Look for the small, subtle signs that can appear pretty much anywhere, and in any situation. The message or the answers you're looking for could be printed on a sign board you just drove past. They could be in that casual remark by a friend, or the lyrics to a song you just heard, or that tarot reading you just had. Just pay attention, and you'll find what you're looking for, including your marching orders.

Here's the bottom line when it comes to discovering what I call your PATH LINE:

If you're good at it and it fulfills you, it's your path line. You've discovered your marching orders!

Haven't found yours yet? Don't fret. Some discover their gifts, their orders, early in life. Others have agreed to gather more life experience before responding to these orders. The timing is perfect, as always. Just know that it's not too late to discover your path line and put your skills to work for the good of all.

REPORTING FOR DUTY

Yes, you do have your marching orders--orders that were written and agreed upon before you were born. You came here to be something extraordinary; yes, to be brilliant. In fact, these orders are encoded in your DNA, in your cellular memory. The danger is not that you might uncover them, use them and fail, but rather that you won't search for them at all. Please continue your search. Do it for you. Do it for all of us. And TRUST that your orders are indeed in there.

DON'T STOP NOW!

It's true that many of us are world-weary. We've been there and done that. And it is very easy for us to give up after years of perceived futility, of wondering and searching. It's so easy for us to accept that we've run out of gas after years of "fitting in" to the status quo. But I urge you to stay strong. Remain diligent. What you are here to do, your marching order, is finally being revealed for many ultra-sensitives, even as you read this material.

Don't give up now when you are so close to the finish line or, rather, the *starting block*. Don't give up now. Because the show's about to begin and you have a front row seat!

IT'S NOW OR NEVER, *REALLY*

Ready or not (and you *are* ready), ultra-sensitives everywhere are being called upon to bring forth all that we have within us, to manifest the marching orders that have lain dormant over the many eons of life in this planet. The time is NOW. The planet needs you. We need you. The fact is we all need *each other*, now more than ever before. If you're ready to be who you came here to be, you've come to the right place at the right time.

Take this simple test:

Which of the following six path lines most closely defines who you really are?

- TEAM LEADER
- INTELLECT
- HEALER
- WARRIOR
- VISIONARY
- TEACHER

To achieve the most accurate results, make sure you factor out current life routines that are not working for you, or that may be working against your authentic self. Dig deeper to that part of you that knows better. It's in there.

Even though you may feel that you fit into several different path lines, find the one that fits you best, the one that best defines who you are overall. This is your primary path line. Underneath your primary path line, list secondary path lines that also describe who you are. Place them in order of priority, that is, start with the one that most closely defines you, moving down to the ones that define you the least. Then step back and take a good look at the qualities that make you who you are.

Once you recognize your path line structure, you will have a better understanding of who you are, and who you can be. You will also gain new insight into what career choices to consider and learn how you can best contribute to your personal growth and the growth of the planet and its inhabitants. Here's to the real you!... Let's get started.

Here are your path line choices:

1. <u>TEAM LEADER</u>

Do you have a knack for taking charge? Are you the one that everyone comes to when something needs to be fixed? Are you the problem solver, the party planner, the organizer? **YOU ARE THE TEAM LEADER.**

YOUR ORDERS: Get into a venue that allows you to lead other ultra-sensitives *and less-sensitives* on their paths.

Many people are on their paths or are searching for their paths but may lack the qualities for organization or leadership. They may also lack vision and the know-how to implement projects, ideas, or events.

The intellect knows exactly how to construct the machines to help improve the lives of others. They can develop ideas and connect the dots like no one's business, but they often need someone to hold their hands to manifest the project. As the TEAM LEADER you can help the intellect put the PC or the box to its best and highest use. It's what you do.

WHERE TO START: Seek jobs, social circles, individuals, organizations, and opportunities that allow you to find your place in the pack and to rise to the role of the team leader. Consider taking on leadership roles at day care or senior centers, spiritual centers, or wherever you feel your take-charge skills will best be utilized.

2. INTELLECT

Do you have a knack for putting things together and taking them apart? Do you always seem to know how things work? Perhaps you can even see schematics in your head. Are you drawn to electronics and machines, always thinking of ways to make things better? Always thinking? **YOU ARE THE INTELLECT.**

YOUR ORDERS: You are here to develop and, with the aid of others, implement the action plans that others will need to fulfill their path line. You are the thinker, rather than the doer. You are always full of ideas.

You know what needs to happen, and why, and you can create the resources that others will need along their journey.

You are the one that designs the PC, the wiring, and the programming and you know exactly why it has to be the way it has to be. You are the technical expert when it comes to developing logistics. You combine logic with your innate intuitive gifts to give others the technology and know-how they really need.

WHERE TO START: Make sure you seek opportunities and employment that stimulate your thinking; otherwise you may lose sight and sense of your path line. Consider an occupation in floral or art design, computer software or hardware design and repair, or research and development firms, but only if they develop products and ideas that can truly benefit others. Website development, flower shops, spiritual development, or holistic think tanks may be a good place to start. However, opportunities to fully express your intellect can be found wherever you may be.

3. HEALER

Have people told you that they feel better just being near you? Do you feel unusually fulfilled when your advice makes someone feel better? Are you drawn toward medicine or the healing arts? **YOU ARE THE HEALER.**

YOUR ORDERS: You know what the human body needs to stay balanced. You have a keen insight into energy movement within the body, even if you do not consciously recognize it. There is often an intense feeling of energy in your hands. A feeling of heat and/or energy may emanate from the rest of the body as well.

You are the one that people will seek out, whether by formal appointment or informally, to get them well. Your may be drawn to hands-on healing techniques. You may even be drawn into allopathic medicine modalities, which over time can develop into a more holistic approach to health.

WHERE TO START: Acknowledge that you have the healing gift. You may choose to work toward a degree, but this is *not* necessary. Take health and healing courses or seminars that you are drawn to. You may find it beneficial to work in a healthcare facility, or become an assistant in a holistic practitioner office, or work in a health store.

Consider developing or attending healing circles in your community, but above all, begin to hone your skills by working on friends or family members on a regular basis. This will help activate your gifts, validate your path line, and give you the inspiration and direction you need to fulfill your contract. Just know that you heal others no matter where you are, what occupation you choose, or in what situation you may find yourself.

4. WARRIOR

Are you overly- protective of your family and friends? Do you attract soft-spoken, timid friends and acquaintances when you go out? Do you tend to feel most comfortable in front of crowds, or step in or speak out when others are maligned in some way? Do you crusade on behalf of others or feel compelled to right the wrongs of the world? **YOU ARE THE WARRIOR**

YOUR ORDERS: You are the change leader. People look to you to forge new paths and to pave the way for their path line evolution, and planetary evolution. Your stature may be greater than most, but size or gender does not matter here. It's your fortitude, determination, and principles that guide your actions and thoughts.

You are the one that other ultra-sensitives will look to, to partner with when it comes to manifesting their path lines. You are the one who can assist the PC intellect in conquering corporate predators.

You find great satisfaction in leading others around obstacles and to the finish line. You protect other ultra-sensitives from opposing forces that seek to sabotage the plan. You are strong willed, focused, and perseverant. You are not in it for the glory, but rather for the satisfaction of making everything right for everybody.

WHERE TO START: Acknowledge your strengths, both physical and mental. Seek out opportunities to intervene on behalf of others, at places such as half-way houses, children's shelters, even detention centers. Convene with local civil rights or animal rights groups. Wherever you go you will find great satisfaction in facilitating the growth and evolution of others.

5. VISIONARY

Do you have a sense of things to come? Do others seek you out because you understand them? Do you understand the bigger picture while others are dwelling on the brush strokes? Do you see and feel things that others do not? Can you sense the feelings, emotions, and energies of others? **YOU ARE THE VISIONARY**

YOUR ORDERS: You came here to help unblock ultra-sensitives who are stuck, to help them remember who they are and, when needed, help them identify their path lines. You are the keeper of hidden secrets and the great revealer of lost memories, and memories yet to be made.

You are the extreme empathic, the great *feeler*. You are the ultra-sensitive of the ultra-sensitive, able to see what each person needs and how to best serve them. You are sought out by all types of energies, so exercising your gifts of discernment is crucial. You offer the vision of past, present, and future possibilities.

You are the one who can advise the PC manufacturer regarding the success potential of a given design or product. Your work guides and assures the success of all the other path lines.

WHERE TO START: You will intuitively place yourself in all walks of life, making yourself available in situations and events where you are most needed. Certainly you can be available in the traditional sense in store-fronts, at psychic fairs, or on the internet; however you may find yourself exercising your gifts in any occupational setting that you choose. Your services are in constant need by the entire gamut of path lines.

You may be particularly drawn to occupations or situations where right-brain creativity is fostered, such as in art galleries, flower shops, or dance and yoga studios, or wherever your intuition tells you to be.

6. TEACHER

Do you have something to say to others? Do you find yourself feeling the need to show others the way? Do you love to write, speak, and express your thoughts and share your skills with the masses? **YOU ARE THE TEACHER**

YOUR ORDERS: Seek out venues where you can share all that you know. You are the disseminator of information that will propel other ultra-sensitives along their paths. You educate and enlighten those who await the teacher. You are the one who appears when the student is ready.

Learning can take place in any setting. Your students can show up in the form of family members, friends, or just someone on the street corner. The curriculum is often pre-determined and resides within the student. Your job is to help them find it and show them how to learn from it. You often teach by example, and you find intense gratification when the information you have helped others remember is manifested for the good of all.

Do not seek out your students, as they will find you. Be prepared to teach wherever and whenever the opportunity is presented, in whichever way the student will best understand.

WHERE TO START: Traditional venues such as pre-schools and public and private institutions are a place to start. However, you may find non-traditional venues more satisfying and rewarding. These can include coffee bars, restaurants, even watering holes. Someone is always waiting to learn something from you, no matter where you are.

Don't be afraid to take a risk with your skills. If you are so inclined, develop a private practice and hang out your teacher shingle proudly. You may call it what you wish: counselor, social worker, life coach. Regardless, you will be ready for your students.

THE SKY IS NOT THE LIMIT

As you begin to manifest and express your path line, don't forget to explore *all* of the skills and abilities within you. Don't be limited by what you read or by what you have been taught by others. There are no limits, except the ones we place on ourselves. As ultra-sensitives, we more than others have been gifted the skills and abilities to achieve greatness. Accept that. There is so much you can do, so much you can achieve if you choose.

12.

Lost My Mind, Came to My Senses

For many ultra-sensitives, coming to grips with who they really are can be a long, challenging, and sometimes even traumatic experience. Yet for others this revelation is a joyful and exhilarating life experience.

No matter how you perceive this revelation of your ultra-sensitivity, it is important to understand that the activation into ultra-sensitivity is a process, a process that slowly but surely changes the way we understand ourselves, and the environment we've come to know as our world.

It can take a bit of time for these notions and realizations to integrate, to become a part of us, to become part of our biology. But the beauty of it all is that there's nothing that you need to do, and, truly, nothing you can do to stop it. Simply allow it to happen and enjoy the journey. It's who you are.

GOT A GRIP

But like any journey, there can be a few bumps in the road along the way. Many ultra-sensitives find themselves experiencing what I call "transition symptoms." These classic feelings and sensations occur while your physical body works to catch up with the energy shifts that are occurring within you. Your body is working overtime to "get a grip" on the new energetic you. It's not uncommon, then, for fledgling ultra-sensitives to find themselves undergoing uncomfortable and sometimes disconcerting physical and emotional changes. In fact, many ultra-sensitives aptly describe these transition symptoms simply this way: It feels as though you've "lost your mind, and come to your senses." In many ways, that's exactly what's happened. And it's a good thing.

Symptoms of "coming to your senses":

- Relationships and people of old may seem unfamiliar or even unimportant.
- Career and job choices seem antiquated and no longer satisfying (if they ever were).
- You feel spacey throughout the day, as though floating through life.
- You start to remember people, places, and things long forgotten.
- Sleep patterns become irregular; some nights you sleep like the dead, others not at all.
- Your perceptive and intuitive abilities become heightened, even profound.
- You may feel compelled to make a physical move into a new home, even a new area.
- You may experience intense cravings to read and explore all things esoteric.

LIVING IN YOUR SENSES

Congratulations! You have begun to leave behind the logical, left-brain, "thinking" world. You have now arrived in the world of the senses, your right brain. This is the feeling, sensing, creative side of your processing apparatus, the mind. And it can be a wonderful place to be. So why not unpack your bags and take off your shoes. You're going to be here a while. Oh, and while you're here, you may want to get used to using your new navigation system, because suddenly you're beginning to feel very intuitive.

Yes, suddenly you may find yourself navigating your way through each moment of your life with a new perspective and using a new tool: your heightened and powerful intuition. That's right. It's your own personal NAV unit. And it's always at work, guiding you to make decisions that are perfect for the new ultra-sensitive you.

At first this right-brain domination can feel a bit unsettling. But soon you will wonder why you ever spent time anywhere else. Many ultra-sensitives describe this new state of being as peaceful, calming, and empowering. Because it is all of that, and more.

DO I KNOW YOU?

Yes, the right-brain shift can be a powerful and pleasurable sensation. Many ultra-sensitives find this shift very nurturing and almost like a sanctuary, so much so that the left side of the brain, the logical, thinking side, may almost seem vacant, empty, useless. That's because suddenly you're spending much less time there and much more time in your creative right brain. Using the left brain less can make performing some of your day-to-day logical tasks, the activities of daily living, much more difficult, even challenging.

You may find that certain functions that were once second nature now require extra effort and attention to accomplish correctly. You may even find yourself having to focus much more intently on a particular logical, left-brain task in order to complete it. This can leave the newly activated ultra-sensitive wondering who they are and where they went, at least for a while.

Signs of spending less time in your left brain:

- Difficulty remembering phone numbers or names of people you used to know well.
- Forgetting for a moment (on a regular basis) what day, date or time it is, or where you are at a given moment.
- Misplacing items that used to be easily at hand at your home or office.
- Difficultly focusing or concentrating.
- Forgetting where you parked the car ten minutes ago.
- Needing directions to your favorite restaurant, the front door, the bathroom, or any other place that you travel often.
- Bumping into things more often than usual.
- More difficulty focusing your vision, or other vision changes.
- Difficulty making simple decisions, like where to eat dinner or what movie to watch.
- Difficulty performing routine tasks at your home or office.
- Feeling like all you really want to do is be creative and free, and not tied to anything.

So now that you've arrived in the right brain world of the ultra-sensitive, there's a dilemma that needs to be resolved. You need to find a way to function in the world outside the front door, a world that was clearly not designed with the ultra-sensitive in mind. What's an ultra-sensitive to do?

HELP! I NEED ADULT SUPERVISION

No, this isn't Alzheimer's, and there's usually nothing physically wrong with you (although if you feel these symptoms have become extreme, do seek medical attention to be sure). These symptoms are a sign that you are operating with all of your senses intact, and in good working order. But it can still make functioning in the day-to-day world a real challenge, so much so that you may suddenly find yourself needing assistance with the tasks that you used to be able to easily accomplish on your own, like driving to and from your office.

Yes, I've heard more than a handful of ultra-sensitives make this remarkable confession:

"Help. I need adult supervision."

Many ultra-sensitives, the gifted mediums, healers and intuitives, including those with celebrity status like James Van Praagh and Doreen Virtue, openly confess that they often need a helping hand to get them to and from their offices and events, and actually employ assistants specifically for that purpose.

And even though you may not be able to employ or even require a full time assistant, I encourage you to ask for a guiding hand, or mind, whenever you may need it. Because trying to navigate through the day when you're in airy-fairy right-brain mode can sometimes be downright detrimental to your well being.

TERRY

Terry was a gifted soul, an ultra sensitive who had definitely arrived. She was a skilled, powerful energy worker and an exceptional intuitive. But she didn't start out that way.

Terry grew up in a home that was quite conservative, one that operated on the traditional societal values. Everything was about logic, money, and business. In fact, by the time Terry reached her twenty-first birthday she was already a successful business owner. And there was no doubt that she could run a business. She had an innate knowledge of how to manage money, manage people, order inventory, and keep customers and vendors happy. Terry could multi-task like nobody's business. She kept her hand in the business world over the next twenty years, operating a number of holistic and health minded ventures with considerable success.

All was well until shortly after her fortieth birthday, when Terry sensed that she was beginning to lose her edge, or so she thought. Oh yes, things were definitely changing, but she didn't yet understand what that meant.

Suddenly her latent intuitive skills began to blossom. She began to see, hear, and feel things about people, and certain situations. She also began to take an interest in Reiki and other energy work, and began to read and devour anything that could feed her hunger for energy healing and the spirit world. It became her life's passion.

Literally over a six-month period, Terry's skills as a hands-on healer went from zero to infinity. Her healing practice and her healing energy soared, and all was well--until she began to notice that certain other aspects of her life were becoming more challenging.

Suddenly she needed to wear reading glasses to get her reading fix. She found herself forgetting where she placed certain things around the house: her car keys, books and notes. She became a bit more clumsy, bumping into things more often than usual. Grocery shopping now required a list, and she now required occasional help to manage her business banking, inventory, and even to book her clients. At first, Terry thought that something was wrong, but all tests were normal, and so was Terry. In fact, everything was right on schedule.

Terry had arrived into her right-brained intuitive and creative self. No longer was left-brain logic controlling her life. Terry was in the process of achieving full activation as an ultra-sensitive, a process that that left her feeling as though she was "losing her mind and coming to her senses."

It didn't take long for Terry to understand and acknowledge that fact. Although always quite independent and self-sufficient, she had the sense to ask for help from her husband from time to time, and he most graciously obliged.

Today Terry maintains a thriving practice in energy healing where she teaches her ultra-sensitive clients what took her thirty years to learn: It's okay, and it's smart, to ask for and receive help from others whenever you need it. Indeed, it's great to be in your "right mind."

HOW DO I MAKE IT THROUGH THE DAY?

As you have likely gathered by now, living the life of an ultra-sensitive can be a beautiful, rewarding, and challenging experience all at once. (Some may have less sparkling descriptors from time-to-time.) . However you view it, being an ultra-sensitive forces us to look at life, and the events within it, in a whole new light. And I mean that literally.

Day-to-day tasks that are managed easily by others can present new and unusual challenges for the ultra-sensitive. Even simple hygiene, health, and relationship issues can be much more difficult to manage than the comparable issue in the less sensitive. After all, as you have seen, our bodies and minds, and our lifestyles, are often unlike most others. For that reason, and many others, you may find yourself in need of a handbook, a quick reference guide on how to get through some of life's little (even colossal) challenges. What you really need is a "How To" guide for the ultra-sensitive.

In fact, over the years many of my ultra-sensitive patients have been clamoring for exactly this type of information. They've been searching everywhere, mostly without success, for a guidebook that was written with the ultra-sensitive in mind.

What follows in the next section of this book is just such a guide; a quick, easy- to-follow collection of information that you can use today, to make your life easier and more fulfilling. So take this opportunity to get the answers to some of the most common and nagging health and life issues you will encounter as an ultra-sensitive. And there are many.

As you do, take heart in knowing you are not alone, and that there are people out there who understand exactly what you're going through. I am simply one of those.

Here's to perfect health and much joy on your life path!

Part II

The Sensitive's Solutions

to

Daily Challenges

How to manage

Mood Swings

Mood swings and depression are a way of life for many, especially during these energetically challenging times, and especially for the ultra-sensitive. That's because we feel everything--pain and suffering, sadness and anger, and so much more--without even knowing that it's happening.

We also have hair-trigger reactions to everything: blood sugar changes, immune shifts, severe food allergies, weather changes, and more. All this ultimately leads to a cascade of events that can create changes in our mood chemicals. And for the ultra-sensitive, the frequency and severity of these chemical changes, the extent of the highs and the lows, can be quite extreme.

One thing's for sure. If you are experiencing mood swings, you are not alone.

Here's the fix:

- Eat more protein. Most people I see in my office are protein deficient, despite how much they weigh. Protein sources include beef, chicken, turkey, fish, eggs, beans, nuts and seeds. Make sure to include a full serving of protein in each of at least three meals daily.
- Clean up your diet. Back off of sugar consumption, easy on the alcohol consumption, and stay clear of artificial sweeteners like aspartame, for starters. These can initiate and aggravate mood swings. Get guidance from a *holistic* nutritionist.
- Drink a whey protein shake every morning in addition to your regular diet. The protein in these supplemental shakes provides the amino acids that are needed to make more of the good mood chemicals, the "happy chemicals" like serotonin, and dopamine and norepinephrine.
- Keep your blood sugars balanced. Mood follows blood sugars, so if your blood sugars crash, your mood will follow suit. That's how it

works. If you have a family history of hypoglycemia or diabetes, take careful strides to keep your sugars balanced. (See: *How to Manage Food Cravings and Hypoglycemia*)

- Take a negativity inventory to see how much negativity is in your life. Make a list of everything that is in and around your life. Examine relationships, jobs, financial stress, everything. Once you've completed your list, stay clear of and/or resolve these negativity triggers. And by all means stay clear of negative people.
- You are an empath. You feel everybody's everything. Know this. Control your aura when in public, especially in large groups or crowds. Keep dark stones on your person, such as tourmaline, hematite, or black onyx, and clear them nightly under running water or in the moonlight on your windowsill. These will help absorb the negative energies so that you don't. (See Part 1: *You Are an Empath.*)
- Start taking *either* SAM-e 400mg once to twice daily *or* 5HTP (5-hydroxytryptophan) 25 to 50mg once to twice daily, last dose at bedtime, or St. John's Wort at doses directed on the bottle. Do not use more than one of these at a time, and *do* stick with these natural antidepressants for at least thirty days to see full results. (Do not use these products while you are taking any prescription anti-depressants.) There are a number of other natural agents that can help boost your mood. Check with your holistic practitioner to find out which ones are best for you.
- Smile more. In fact, make yourself smile at least ten times per day, and especially when you're feeling your lowest. When you stimulate the smile muscles, chemical changes are set in motion that can boost your mood. Try it. It works!
- Get food allergy tested through applied kinesiology. Food allergies in the ultra-sensitive can cause an assault on your tender immune system, and throw all of your sensitive organs out of balance. This immune system jolt creates a cascade of events within your body, often leading to mood chemical imbalances.
- Avoid the use of prescription anti-depressants when possible. They tend to blunt your emotional sensitivity, your intuition, and your other sensitive gifts, making their use counter-productive for ultra-sensitives. That doesn't mean you should *never* use prescription anti-depressants, but use them only if natural methods at the proper doses do not bring enough symptomatic relief.

- And remember; unlike what popular medical protocol would have you believe, you don't necessarily have to stay on prescription anti-depressants forever, and you shouldn't. Your body and mind can heal and change with time, and often does as you evolve into your sensitivity. If and when you feel that you're ready to try life without prescription medicines, or if you're ready to correct the underlying causes of your mood, seek the guidance of your holistic practitioner. Either way, do not stop these medicines cold turkey.
- Women, if you're experiencing depression or mood swings, get your hormones checked promptly. Low progesterone levels, which can occur at any age, is often the culprit.
- Limit your exposure to all electrical devices such as cell phones, computers, fluorescent lighting, high power devices, and the like. These EMF-emitting devices can easily throw your ultra sensitive immune system into a tizzy and create mood chemical imbalances.
- Clear yourself of entities. Entities are unseen energy attachments from disembodied souls, and they are often attracted to sensitive light beings, like you. Negative entity attachments are a significant and under-recognized cause of both acute and long term mood issues. Seek the guidance of a qualified energy worker to help clear these attachments promptly.

Sensitive's summary:

Ultra-sensitives feel everything, and hence are often emotionally fragile. If you are suffering from chronic mood swings, know that they are often not of your own making, and that they can be corrected. Start working on it today.

How to manage

Colds and Flu

We all get sick now and again. But because ultra-sensitives have ultra-sensitive immune systems, the usual planetary "bugs" can make us sicker and keep us down longer than others. Even a small cut or a break in the skin can send our tender immune systems and the rest of our organs into hyper-drive, and that can lay us out for days, weeks, or longer.

Yes, for many ultra-sensitives these simple quirks of life, like picking up a little bug, can become a big deal. The trick? Take extra care of yourself in every way, and bolster your immune system carefully and consciously.

Here's the fix:

- Stay clear of sick people. Now this may sound like an easy task, but when you're a healer, or are propelled into the workplace or forced into unavoidable social situations, protecting yourself from infections can be a full time job.
- Do NOT get any flu vaccine, or any vaccine, *ever*. Period. These vaccines often contain the actual live virus and other toxic ingredients that can stir up your body in unexplainable ways, and can potentially maim you for life. Just say NO.
- Eat plenty of onions, garlic, and mushrooms as part of your daily meal plan. Include plenty of dark-colored vegetables like broccoli, kale, zucchini, and spinach.
- Consume plenty of protein in your diet. If you are vegan or vegetarian, make sure you calculate your daily protein intake based on your body weight, and supplement accordingly. You are an ultra-sensitive. You're burning through more protein and calories than you realize, just by existing within these harsh planetary energies. Supplement your normal diet with a whey protein shake once or twice daily. The immune factors in whey will help keep you feeling tip-top.

- Stay hydrated. Drink plenty of distilled water. Distilled water keeps your body alkaline, and an alkaline state can help keep illness away. How much water should you drink? Take your body weight in pounds and divide by two. That's the number of ounces of water you should strive to drink every day. Start now. Here's a toast to hydration and health!
- Take 500 to 1000mg of buffered vitamin C once or twice daily to keep your adrenal glands and immune system strong and to keep any viral load under control.
- Take n-acetyl-cysteine 900mg once or twice daily to boost your immune system and to gently detoxify your body.
- Use natural immune boosting vitamins and supplements as you intuit, but cautiously, and only if you are certain you're not allergic or sensitive to them.
- Herbs like astragalus, echinacea, elderberry, barley greens, and mushroom derivatives are powerful immune stimulants. But for many ultra-sensitive, these immune stimulants can actually do more harm than good, by pushing your sensitive immune system over the edge. In many cases they can trigger or make worse the autoimmune symptoms of chronic fatigue, rheumatoid arthritis, Lupus, and others. Use them only as directed, and only if other immune or healing modalities do not work
- Stay positive. Your "mooditude" has everything to do with keeping your immune system and the rest of your body strong and vital.
- Talk to your organs. Yes, it may sound silly, but talking to your organs on a regular basis can perk them up and help keep them healthy, just as talking to plants or playing gentle music for them keeps them healthy and vital. Go ahead. Your organs are always listening. Tell them how strong and vital they are and how grateful you are to have them working so hard for you. You may be surprised at the results.
- Don't be a martyr. If you sense that an infection is overwhelming you and your immune system see your healthcare practitioner promptly and get on antibiotics as prescribed. Sometimes we all need a little help from modern medicine.

Sensitive's summary:

If you give your immune system and the rest of your body the right nutrients and support, it will serve you long and serve you well.

How to manage

Food Cravings and Hypoglycemia

Ultra-sensitives are more prone to blood sugar swings and hypoglycemia (low blood sugar) than the rest of the population. That's because of our unique sensitivity to foods and our dynamic and powerful energy swings, which can, of course, lead to powerful and dynamic blood sugar swings.

As ultra-sensitives, we are bombarded by so many types of energies and life challenges during our day that we can burn through our nutrients very quickly. That leaves us craving and seeking out comfort foods, not just to compensate for these nutrient losses but also to sooth us. For some it's salty food, for others it's ground beef or protein. Yet for most of us it's the sweet stuff we're searching for. And let's face it. It's yummy!

Here's the fix:

- Make sure you eat no less than five or six smaller meals each day.
- Include some form of protein in each of those meals. They don't have to be huge portions, just make sure some of the following are in each meal: chicken; turkey; fish; beans; beef; vegetables, the darker the better (easy on carrots, corn, and potatoes); and nuts and seeds (preferably walnuts and almonds, which tend to be less allergenic).
- Consume a whey or soy protein shake once or twice daily, mixed with almond milk, in addition to your regular meals. Make sure you're not allergic to soy. About half the population is.
- Start taking chromium picolinate 200mcg twice or three times daily, ½ hour before meals. Chromium can help balance blood sugars and help build lean body mass.
- Take a high quality broad-spectrum probiotic blend (the "good bacteria") before food every day to help fight Candida overgrowth. Ultra-sensitives are more prone to Candida infections, and Candida

infections can cause an intense craving for sweets, and cause hypoglycemia.

- Start using a high potency, broad spectrum digestive enzyme half way through two or three of your larger meals daily. This will help improve digestion and absorption of your nutrients and help minimize blood sugar swings and the resultant food cravings.
- If you feel a craving coming on, drink a good size glass of water and reach for the cut-up celery or the nuts and seeds you have on standby in the pantry. You do have celery cut up, right? (It's great for calming your nerves and balancing blood pressure, too.)
- Don't be afraid to give in to your craving for an occasional nibble of your favorite sweets when your willpower has gone galactic. An occasional morsel of your favorite flavors won't hurt you, and, in fact, complete deprivation of these treats can actually make matters worse. If your nibbles turn into gorging, refer back to the top of this page. Enjoy. You deserve it!

Sensitive's summary:

Eating more protein more often will balance your cravings and blood sugars, and you will feel more balanced and satisfied physically, emotionally, and spiritually.

How to manage

Anxiety and Panic

Are you feeling a little edgy? Perhaps you feel a constant, low level of apprehension. You are an empath, a sensitive receiver of energies. That's what ultra-sensitives do. You feel the energies of others. You feel the energies from electronic devices, the global angst, and the anxiety and stress of your next-door neighbor, co-worker, friend or family member. Whew! The list goes on and on.

It's very easy, then, for ultra-sensitives to become overloaded with energy input. When this happens, feelings of anxiety and panic can set in. But just because you are a powerful receiver doesn't mean you have to let anxiety and panic control your life. Turn the tables.

Here's the fix:

- Correct your thyroid function. Undiagnosed *hyper*thyroidism is one of the key causes of panic and anxiety. If you're taking a prescription thyroid medicine like levothyroxine (Synthroid) or Armour Thyroid, consider these as likely suspects for causing your anxiety. This holds true even if thyroid blood tests are "normal". That's because blood tests for thyroid function are often inaccurate and unreliable indicators of thyroid function, especially in ultra-sensitives. Work with your holistic practitioner to help you taper off of these agents and to bolster your thyroid function naturally.
- If you're taking any other types of prescription medicines, such as blood pressure medicines or hormone supplements, don't rule these out as possible anxiety triggers as well. Anxiety is a common side effect with many of these.
- Balance your hormones naturally. Progesterone, estrogen and testosterone imbalances can easily lead to panic and anxiety, even if you're having no other hormonal symptoms. Work with your holistic

practitioner to check and balance them, using applied kinesiology for most accurate results.

- Eat plenty of protein. Many people, and especially ultra-sensitives, are protein deficient. Eat plenty of turkey, fish, beef, beans, chicken, and eggs. Supplement with a whey protein shake every morning in addition to your regular meals. If you are vegan or vegetarian, supplement with a suitable protein supplement. The amino acids in protein help produce more of the brain chemicals that keep us calm.
- Balance your blood sugars with chromium picolinate. Start with 200mcg twice daily before meals. Hypoglycemia is a classic trigger of panic attacks and anxiety. Balance your sugars and you will feel better.
- Take inositol 500 to 1500mg, three or four times daily to help calm your mind. Inositol is a B vitamin, non-habit forming and helps lower high testosterone levels, to help keep you calm and help you sleep. You can safely use 8000 to 10,000mg daily, or more if needed, without any negative effects. It's also a great natural anti-depressant.
- Correct your low mood. Low mood is almost always accompanied by feelings of anxiety or panic, and is usually the result of low serotonin levels. Taking 5HTP (5-hydroxytryptophan) can help restore low serotonin levels, a common finding among ultra-sensitives as well as the rest of the general population. Start with 25 to 50mg once or twice daily and adjust the dose carefully according to the guidance of a qualified holistic practitioner.
- Take a B complex, 50 to 100mg, daily with breakfast. The B vitamins are natural tranquilizers and will help keep your nervous system in tip-top shape.
- Start fish oil 1000mg twice daily with food. Work up to 2000 to 3000mg once or twice daily over several weeks. Fish oil slows and regulates nerve impulses to help keep you focused and relaxed. It may take several weeks to see full effect, so please be patient. If you take prescription blood thinners like Plavix, aspirin, or Coumadin, get guidance from your practitioner before you start.
- Supplements like GABA (gamma-aminobutyric acid), valerian, l-theanine, magnesium and others can also be helpful in controlling the symptoms of anxiety and panic. Check with your holistic practitioner to determine which ones may be best for your situation.

- Reduce the input in all areas of your life, wherever possible. Take a careful look at all of your life routines. Evaluate their true importance in your life, and then begin to unload your plate as much as possible. This can include limiting some methods of communication that may be cluttering your mind, such as texting, cell phone calls, and excess TV and Internet use. Sometimes being less connected is a good thing, and eliminating all that extra EMF exposure is also beneficial.
- Stay clear of negative people, high-pressure situations, and stressful relationships. Start by mending the relationship with yourself. Be good to yourself and become more patient and understanding with yourself. You're ultra sensitive to so many things. Honor that.
- Catch yourself whenever you are holding your breath, throughout the day. Holding your breath can quickly and easily lead to anxiety and mood changes. Breathe fully and regularly, and *through your nose* whenever possible. This will increase oxygenation and help keep you calm and relaxed. Start making nose breathing your breathing habit.

Sensitive's summary:

You are a powerful and highly sensitive receiver. Make sure your tuner is operating properly to filter out unnecessary static and undesirable energy frequencies that have become part of your daily routine. This will help keep anxiety and panic in check.

How to manage

Hormonal Imbalances and Fibroid Cysts

Hormonal imbalances are common phenomena, especially among women, and especially among ultra-sensitive women. And you are sensitive. That doesn't mean that men don't have hormonal issues. We do. But they don't compare to the hormonal restructuring pandemic that appears to be underway for the female gender. So many women are running around with progesterone, estrogen, and testosterone levels that are way out of balance.

Low progesterone levels can occur at any age, even during puberty, but as ultra-sensitive women enter the age of the "pause" falling progesterone levels are the word of the day. And if you've had a hysterectomy, even a partial hysterectomy, you can count on low progesterone levels. This can lead to weight gain, depression, headache, migraines, low libido, and so much more.

Then there's estrogen, the infamous female hormone. There's been plenty of publicity surrounding the issue of low estrogen and hot flashes. But that pales in comparison to the silent pandemic of HIGH estrogen that's afflicting millions of unknowing women around the globe. Unchecked, high estrogen can cause ovarian cysts, fibrocystic breasts, endometriosis, and, ultimately, cancer of the ovaries and breasts. Let's get balanced today.

Here's the fix:

- Start by using topical progesterone cream, available without a prescription from your holistic practitioner or your health food store. Start with ¼ to ½ teaspoonful applied nightly at bedtime, as directed. Women who are still cycling regularly should supplement on days twelve through twenty-six of their menstrual cycle only. (Day one is the first day of bleeding) Women who are no longer cycling or are cycling irregularly should apply the cream on calendar days one through twenty-one of each month. This will help raise low progesterone levels and help lower high estrogen levels if they exist. It's very important that you have your hormone levels rechecked approximately three to four weeks after beginning this therapy, and preferably through applied kinesiology. If you're not sure how to start, or if you are using hormonal birth control or other hormonal products, talk with your holistic practitioner first.

- If you suffer from fibrocystic breasts or ovarian cysts and estrogen levels are still elevated, in addition to the above add DIM (di-indolylmethane) or any high-quality blend of indole-3-carbinole. This will help reduce estrogen levels even further, and help shrink cystic growth. In some cases it may be necessary to add calcium-D-glucarate, another natural estrogen modulator, if estrogen levels still remain high. Use these products as directed by your practitioner.
- Take flax lignans in capsule form as directed on the bottle. The brand I use in my practice is NutraFlax. It has been quite effective in breaking down fibroid cysts and lowering estrogen for my patients, and can also help relieve constipation and improve bowel function.
- Eat plenty of cruciferous vegetables like broccoli, cabbage, and brussels sprouts. These contain natural forms of DIM and other ingredients to keep estrogen levels balanced and your cells healthy.
- Clean all produce thoroughly before consuming it, in order to remove any pesticide residues. These pesticides often contain estrogen-like substances that can cause estrogen troubles. Make an inexpensive produce cleanser by adding one capful of bleach to a sink full of water. Let everything soak for twenty minutes. Rinse thoroughly with water, and let dry. You may also use commercially available produce cleansers as directed.
- If you are experiencing anxiousness, edginess, increased facial hair growth, acne, or lowering of your vocal range, or if you have high cholesterol levels, there's a good chance your testosterone levels are elevated. Start taking inositol, 500 to 1000mg, two to three times daily and before bed to help balance them. It's inexpensive, safe, and not addicting.
- PCOS, or polycystic ovary syndrome, is a major health crisis among all women, especially women of childbearing years. With PCOS, progesterone levels are typically very low, estrogen and testosterone

levels are very high, and thyroid function is typically out of balance. In addition to ovarian and breast cysts, this condition is complicated by blood sugar and appetite changes, acne and skin outbreaks, facial hair growth, weight issues, and more. Natural remedies are available to help reduce the symptoms of PCOS. Talk to your practitioner to discuss a natural protocol, or reach my office.

- Last, and absolutely NOT least, make sure you're not over-nurturing others and *under-nurturing* yourself. Over time, this kind of behavior *will* create high estrogen levels in your body. Estrogen levels are often higher in women who tend to give too much of themselves to others, or those who emotionally neglect themselves. This is based on the premise that all physical changes begin in the emotional field. And they do. This is a classic example of emotions at work. Ultra-sensitive women take heed; if you want to stay hormonally balanced, take exceptional care of your emotional self. You must balance the intake with the output. Give of yourself to others only in moderation. Don't give yourself away. Begin this practice today, and you will begin to feel better physically and emotionally. It works.

MEN HAVE HORMONES, TOO

Men can also experience hormone imbalances that can affect prostate health, libido, mood, energy, and more. In fact, what I have noticed over the years of checking the hormones of ultra-sensitive men is that they tend to have naturally higher progesterone and estrogen levels, and a more favorable progesterone to testosterone ratio. This would make sense since progesterone is one of the key "soft and nurturing" hormones. This ratio also seems to be a protection against prostate cancer and other testosterone driven health conditions like high cholesterol and heart disease. It's a good thing.

Men, don't be shy. If you sense your hormones are out of balance, visit with your holistic practitioner for guidance. Natural help is available.

Sensitive's summary:

The process of balancing the hormones of sensitive women and men is as unique as the individuals who carry them. Everyone is

different. But it can be done. Start by getting your hormones checked by a qualified holistic practitioner.

How to manage

Candida Infections

Millions of unsuspecting people are running around with toxic yeast-like organisms worming around in their sensitive bodies. It's called Candida albicans, or affectionately known as just plain Candida. If you suffer from chronic foggy-headedness, digestive problems like acid reflux and irritable bowel, joint and muscle aches, memory lapses, and a sweet tooth that could choke a horse, there's a very good chance you have an infestation of Candida.

Candida is a part of the normal micro-organism flora of ultra-sensitives and less-sensitives alike, and it resides in many different parts of our bodies. But it can be triggered to grow out of control by physical and emotional stress, poor diet choices, prescription antibiotics, and poor nutrition, and more.

Candida infections are a chronic condition that affects millions, but because of our delicate immune systems, ultra-sensitives seem to grab the market's share of Candidiasis, and they tend to have more severe and debilitating effects from the classic symptoms.

Here's the fix:

- Stay clear of fruits, fruit juices, and all sugary foods and pastries. Stop drinking sodas, all sodas. Consume alcohol only in moderation. Ease back on vinegar and breads and all white flour products. These and many other foods help these feisty bugs proliferate, and provide the food they need to have a field day with the vulnerable ultra-sensitive. Stick with a solid anti-Candida diet regimen available on the Internet or from your holistic practitioner.
- Start taking a high potency multi-strain probiotic, the "friendly bacteria" that squelches this unfriendly one, at the maximum dose every day, twenty to thirty minutes before meals. Stay on this

continuously and for no less than six months. It's also great preventive medicine for many other digestive and immune conditions, so stay with it on a daily basis.

- Start on caprylic acid capsules as directed on the bottle or by your practitioner, and stay with this for at least ninety days. There are many combination products available at your health food store that contains this ingredient and other anti-fungal ingredients that can be beneficial. If you don't know where to start, check in with your holistic practitioner.
- Use a broad-spectrum digestive enzyme halfway through two or three of your bigger meals each day. This will help you digest carbohydrates and other nutrients more effectively and reduce the potential for a Candida infection.
- Eat plenty of garlic and onions, and plenty of fresh vegetables like cabbage, broccoli, and brussels sprouts.
- Drink at least ten to twelve glasses of distilled water every day to help flush out toxins and keep you well "oiled".
- Make sure you've resolved any liver imbalances and constipation issues. Getting your digestive and elimination organs fully functional is the key to expediting the cure for Candida.
- Candida is an opportunistic organism, meaning that it tends to spread faster when given the opportunity, such as in people with weakened immune systems and those who are poorly nourished. That's why it's imperative to NOT skip meals and to maintain a healthy diet, including plenty of protein.
- Reduce the physical and emotional stress in your life. Remember, you're an ultra-sensitive. Stress is even more detrimental to us, and opens the doors for infections like this one.
- Many people have heavy metal toxicity from mercury exposure through their dental work, or through environmental exposures. Mercury and other heavy metal toxins predispose the ultra-sensitive immune system to Candida over-growth. Before you begin a full-blown Candida cleanse, have your holistic practitioner check your heavy metal load through kinesiology, and clear that first. Otherwise Candida infections will be very difficult to clear, or can quickly return. (See: *How to Deal with Environmental Toxicity)*

- Women, if you get frequent vaginal yeast infections, you likely have a systemic Candida albicans yeast infection. Begin the above regimen promptly and these symptoms should begin to subside.

It can take weeks or months, even a year or more to fully clear a Candida infection, depending on the vitality of your immune system. Be patient and diligent and you will feel better.

Sensitive's summary:

Ultra-sensitives are uniquely sensitive to all kinds of infectious processes. Candida is just another. But now you have the power to banish these bugs. Use it.

How to manage

Foggy Headedness

Do you frequently find yourself in a daze? Do you feel disoriented throughout the day? Does your reality often feel surreal? Maybe you have a hard time concentrating. Do you often feel like you need adult supervision? Welcome to the life of the ultra-sensitive.

Ultra-sensitives are often considered by others to be "airy fairy." The truth is, they're right. Many ultra-sensitives do feel "airy fairy." Our minds are flighty, expansive, and often operating in multiple dimensions, on multiple projects, both consciously and subconsciously. It's part of who we are. It's a symptom of our sensitivity. Still, it can make functioning in the world outside the front door very challenging.

Here's the fix:

- Balance your blood sugars. Start by easing back on your consumption of sugar. We all get sugar cravings from time to time. If yours are out of control, start on chromium picolinate 200mcg two or three times daily before meals. This will help balance sugars and your mood, and your concentration.
- Make sure you're getting plenty of protein in your diet. This includes beef, chicken, turkey, fish, beans, eggs, nuts and seeds, as well as vegetable protein. If you can't eat enough protein or if you are vegetarian, use a whey protein shake every morning for breakfast, in addition to your regular food. Vegetarians and vegans are almost always protein deficient, and hence often require protein supplementation. Bump up your protein consumption with pea or hemp protein or other suitable forms every day. You'll feel better.
- Eat beef. Beef is very grounding and can quickly bring you back to Earth when you need to be there. And believe me, when you are an

ultra-sensitive you need to be grounded, maybe even tethered to the kitchen table. And don't concern yourself with the whole cholesterol debacle. Food is typically not the reason your cholesterol is high. It has much more to do with planetary stress and liver congestion than anything else.

- Perform a Candida cleanse. Candida infestation classically causes foggy headedness, and many ultra-sensitives have an overgrowth of Candida due to a combination of stress, poor diet choices, and their super-sensitive immune systems. Clean it up. Start by following a solid Candida elimination program. (See: *How to Manage Candida Infections*)

Don't see the foggy head as so much of a problem. Often it is a symptom that you're very tuned in to other realms and higher frequencies. And that's a good thing. So go ahead. Be intuitive. Be out there. Go where others have only dreamed of going. And may your force stay with you!

On a more clear-headed, grounded note, please understand that there may be times that we truly do need adult supervision. As we become more and more sensitive, critical left-brain thinking may become tricky. This can be life-endangering, especially when we are operating dangerous equipment like cars, or knives and other sharp objects. If you need left-brain assistance, ask a friend, or family member, to give you a hand. This author does on a regular basis. It's not CRS syndrome. It's your gift. (See Part I: *Lost My Mind, Came to My Senses*)

Sensitive's summary:

Being foggy headed is often a signpost that your sensitivity is escalating. Honor that. Then start using your powerful new radar system to take you to new realms and new horizons.

How to manage

Chronic Fatigue

We are sensitive souls. It's no surprise, then, that most people that are diagnosed with Chronic Fatigue and Immune Dysfunction Syndrome (CFIDS) are ultra-sensitive. And most of them are women. That's because members of the female gender, in general, tend to be more emotionally open and vulnerable to the energies on the planet. But ultra-sensitive men, beware. You're not immune.

The constant bombardment of environmental energy onto the porous energy of ultra-sensitives ultimately drains the adrenal glands, the immune system, and other organ systems; creating a permanent genetic realignment that traditional healthcare refers to as CFIDS. Other factors that can trigger this condition include heavy metal toxicity, especially mercury as the result of mercury amalgam implants or mercury removal procedures, and the Epstein-Barr virus as the result of mononucleosis infection, as well as a host of other planetary toxins.

The resultant symptoms include exhaustion, depression, muscle aches and pains, liver congestion, sleep cycle disruption, blood sugar swings, digestive problems, and more.

Whether we like it or not, these genetic changes are part of a global evolutionary shift in our makeup, something that's actually part of our soul plan. The good news is that these transitional symptoms can be subdued.

Here's the fix:

- Stop pushing so hard, physically and emotionally, especially you women. There's nothing you need to prove to anyone, including yourself. Accept who you are graciously and without fear of judgment by others. Physical and emotional pushing puts undue stress on your sensitive organs and your energy fields. Once you truly acknowledge that you have nothing to prove to anyone and you act accordingly, many of the symptoms will begin to subside on their own.

- Eat more protein. You've heard this before. That includes plenty of beef, chicken, turkey, fish, beans, eggs, and vegetables. Consume some of these in each of five or six small meals every day. This will help balance blood sugars and improve your stamina.
- Supplement with natural medicines according to your symptoms. Below is the basic regimen for the rebalancing of CFIDS. Other products may also be appropriate. Check with your holistic practitioner to see what's right for you.
    - **Muscle aches**: Magnesium and malic acid combination as per bottle directions
    - **Mood**: SAM-e 400mg once to twice daily for at least sixty days
    - **Exhaustion**: NADH 10mg daily for at least ninety days
    - **Blood sugar swings**: Chromium picolinate 200mcg two or three times daily
    - **Energy and immune balance**: Whey protein shake once or twice daily
    - **Sleep**: Melatonin 1 to 2mg, nightly before bed
    - **Liver health and virus reduction**: Maitake/Shitake/Reishi mushroom blend per bottle directions
    - **Adrenal stamina**: Pantothenic acid 500mg two or three times daily

- Protect yourself from electrics, negative people, and any energies that feel grating to yours. Carry dark stones at all times: hematite, black onyx, or black tourmaline. Use EMF protectors on all electronic devices.
- Avoid strenuous exercise, including certain types of yoga. Over-exercising in an attempt to stay fit or to lose weight or inches often backfires for the ultra-sensitive, triggering yet another autoimmune cycle of symptoms we know as CFIDS. Be gentle on your sensitive body.
- Perform a heavy-metal cleanse under the supervision of your holistic practitioner. Heavy metals and other toxins are often key triggers for

the immune storms that trigger CFIDS and other autoimmune disorders. This can include exposures to mercury, cadmium, barium, thallium, plutonium and many other heavy metals in the environment. A foot detoxification bath performed on a regular basis can also be very useful in reducing heavy metal and toxin loads and improving your energy.

- Avoid daytime napping. Make sure you get between six and nine hours of REM sleep nightly. No more and no less. If you need help getting your sleep cycles regulated, visit with your holistic practitioner.
- Know your limit when it comes to performing healing work on others. Screen your clients carefully to avoid taking on those with intense negative energy, those with extreme imbalances, or those loaded with entities. Be discerning when it comes to choosing your patients and don't give out more energy than you can quickly restore. Know when to say when.
- Clear yourself regularly with a salt and soda bath. That's ¼ cup each of baking soda and non-iodized salt in a tub full of warm water. Soak yourself thoroughly for about twenty minutes whenever you feel you need to be energetically cleared, as often as every night.
- We wake up each day with a certain number of "credits" in our energy bank. Each day, before you go into the world outside the front door, carefully plan how you wish to spend yours. Choose to spend your energy on the things that bring you the most joy and fulfillment, and avoid the rest.

Sensitive's summary:

Chronic fatigue syndrome and its classic symptoms are the ultimate expression of just how sensitive you are. Accept the opportunity to rest, knowing full well that CFIDS is nothing more than an expression of who you really are, and who you are in the process of becoming.

How to manage

Gas and Constipation

Now this may seem to be an innocuous subject but, for many people, having 24/7 gas (AKA flatulence) and non-stop constipation is a real issue, and very uncomfortable. Ultra-sensitives tend to have exquisitely sensitive digestive and immune systems, making the problems of gas and constipation even more distracting and annoying.

Holding gas is no fun, it's embarrassing when it sneaks out, and it can also be quite painful. This can also lead to more issues with constipation, creating a vicious cycle of gastric discomfort.

Here's the fix:

- Take a broad-spectrum digestive enzyme halfway through two or three of your larger meals every day. Taking lactase or bromelain by itself is not enough for most ultra-sensitives. Check with your health food store or your holistic practitioner's office for the best choices for you.
- Add a probiotic combination, the friendly bacteria, and take it daily as per the directions on the package. This blend should contain no less than five different strains of these healthy bacteria.
- Yes, you may choose to also eat yogurt to ingest these friendly bacteria, but make sure it's the plain organic variety. If you are allergic to dairy, and most people are, eat the yogurt because you enjoy it, not because you need more friendly bacteria. You'll get all you need by supplementing with the probiotic pill. Avoid probiotic-fortified yogurts such as Activia, and DanActive, since these contain several unnecessary and unhealthy ingredients. Instead, use plain organic yogurt available at your local health food store.

- Eat fresh pineapple or papaya to improve digestion. These two fruits contain natural digestive enzymes that can help stabilize your sensitive digestive tract.
- Food allergies are almost always implicated in gas and constipation, especially in people who are as sensitive as you are. Get food allergy tested through your local holistic practitioner, and then follow your new diet protocol. You'll feel better from the inside out.
- Take one tablespoonful of apple cider vinegar in four ounces of distilled water once or twice daily, before food. This can help improve digestion, squelch gastric reflux, calm the gallbladder, and reduce the production of gas. Lemon juice in water can be equally effective.
- For ultra-sensitives, these and other digestive problems are a signal that your solar plexus chakra, the energy center where you intuit your daily decisions, may not be clear or working well. An energy treatment from a qualified energy worker will often get things moving again, in more ways than one.
- Paying conscious attention to your intuition and using it regularly will also help you feel better. And don't forget a good belly laugh now and again. That, and full diaphragmatic nose breathing--that is, from your abdomen--will also help keep your digestive tract happy.

For constipation: Stay clear of dairy products, including cheese. These are constipating. Instead, eat plenty of vegetables, the darker the color the better. Easy on corn. Eat plenty of beans and legumes, and nuts and seeds. Drink ten to twelve glasses of distilled water every day, and make sure you're getting thirty minutes of uninterrupted exercise every day. Walking is a great way to accomplish this. Magnesium can also keep your bowels moving. Start with 200mg once to twice daily with food. Avoid taking calcium without magnesium. Taking calcium by itself can be constipating.

Last but certainly not least, work to become less structured and rigid in your daily life, and become more giving of your time and money. Your constipation and your well being will improve, and you'll feel better, everywhere.

For gas: Yes, beans and the cruciferous vegetables can cause gas, but they're also very healthy for your digestive tract and everything else. Once you start on your digestive enzyme these symptoms should subside. Don't hold onto trapped gas. This can cause all kinds of abdominal discomfort.

Gas is a symptom that your body is trying to clear something (other than methane gas). Take a hard look at what emotional issues are coming up for processing and make all efforts to process and clear them, whatever they are. We are upon the "Days of Clearing" on this planet. If you need help identifying what you're holding onto, contact your holistic practitioner for a clearing session. Just get rid of it.

Sensitive's summary:

Experiencing gas and constipation is no laughing matter. And for ultra-sensitives these two symptoms are often a sign, a gift to you, to let you know that an adjustment in the way you digest life may be in order. With better digestion comes a more fulfilling and healthy life, and you deserve that.

How to manage

Stress Headaches

We have no choice right now. Ultra-sensitives have to deal with all the stressors on the planet, just like everyone else. The workplace, crime in our streets, difficult relationships, money issues, constant deadlines (FYI, we create these ourselves), you name it. It feels like we're under constant pressure, physically, emotionally, in every way. For many ultra-sensitives, the result of all of this daily pressure is a stress headache.

Sure, there are many causes for headaches other than life stress, including hormone imbalances, food allergies, hay fever allergies, high blood pressure, and more, and you should do whatever is necessary to balance these issues. But whether it's a stress headache or any other type of headache, the result is still the same: debilitating pain and discomfort.

Here's the fix:

- Breathe. That's right. Many people hold their breath when they become stressed. Catch yourself holding your breath, and start breathing through your nose. Practice nose breathing every day and all of the time. Why not start now? Go ahead, breathe. Make nose breathing a part of your daily routine and you'll help relieve the pressure in your head.
- Take careful inventory of all the routines in your life that are making you feel pressured. Your job? Your relationship? Your over-booked Day Timer? Why not seek simpler ways to accomplish whatever it is you're trying to accomplish. Remember, in truth, we determine our own schedules and routines. Don't like yours? Change it. Today.
- Shield yourself from excess EMF (electromagnetic field) exposure. Translated, that means minimize or eliminate exposure to computer screens, cell phones, iPads, cordless phones, and bright lights, especially fluorescents lights. Fluorescent lights can disrupt your

immune system and can easily trigger headaches, especially in the susceptible ultra-sensitive. Use EMF deflectors on these devices, available inexpensively most anywhere.

- If you read a lot, minimize eyestrain. If you wear glasses or contacts, make sure your prescription or OTC strength is still appropriate for you. If you don't wear glasses, get your eyes checked. You may need them. (See: *How to Manage the Aging Process*)
- Close and rest your eyes whenever possible. That doesn't mean you have to nap during the day, just take a rest from optical inputs. Excessive input from any source is a stress headache waiting to happen.
- Make sure your chakras are open, clear, and balanced, especially your throat, third eye, and crown chakras. When these chakras are blocked for any reason (and as ultra-sensitives we have many reasons), you can count on a stress headache, or *any type* of headache. Treat yourself to a chakra-balancing session with your favorite practitioner. You'll feel better.
- Make sure you clear all the toxins from your body. Heavy metals, chemical exposures, and the like will clog your liver and create potential for headaches and more. Balance and clear your liver using milk thistle containing supplements as directed. (See: *How to Manage Environmental Toxicity*)
- Catch yourself if you are clenching your jaw. You can call it TMJ. I call it angst. Either way, jaw clenching is notorious for causing headache pain. Start supplementing with calcium and magnesium to help relax those muscles, and start using inositol, 500 to 1000mg, several times daily to help keep you calm and relaxed.
- Balance your hormones. Low progesterone levels and other hormonal imbalances are classic headache triggers, especially for migraine sufferers. Get your hormones balanced through applied kinesiology (AK), and your headaches can become a thing of the past.
- Quit thinking so much. Get out of your left brain. Instead, start expressing yourself through right-brain activities. Sing, dance, write, paint, or do whatever it is that makes you feel creative.
- Supplementing with white willow bark, boswellia, feverfew and other natural analgesics, alone or in combination, can also help relieve headache pain and inflammation. If these are not fully effective use ibuprofen or acetaminophen, but only as directed, in minimal doses,

and only for a short time. If your headache persists, check in with your healthcare practitioner, just to be sure.

Sensitive's summary:

The overwhelming pressures of society can wreak havoc on a multi-dimensional ultra-sensitive like you. Do whatever you can to minimize input, and you can help keep the headaches at bay.

How to manage

Low Thyroid Function

Millions of people, mostly women suffer from low energy, hair loss, weight gain, dry skin, and other symptoms as a result of low thyroid function. Ultra-sensitives are even more susceptible to low energy levels because of our uniquely sensitive immune system, and our sensitivity to outside energy influences. In other words, our metabolism is more easily disrupted than others.

As a result of these disruptions, millions are taking thyroid supplements like levothyroxine (Synthroid) and Armour thyroid to help boost their thyroid function when in fact they have a completely normal and functional thyroid gland. To make matters worse, these prescription thyroid boosters often result in unwanted side effects like anxiety, insomnia, hypertension, even osteoporosis.

This type of supplementation is mostly unnecessary. That's because there's usually something *else* going on that's causing the thyroid to become, well…lazy. Correcting the underlying causes of hypothyroidism can avert the need for these prescriptions, and their potential side effects.

Here's the fix:

- Get your hormones balanced ASAP! Low progesterone levels almost universally leads to low active thyroid hormone (T3), resulting in low thyroid function. Checking your hormones through applied kinesiology provides accurate and quick results. Bolster low progesterone levels with topical progesterone cream, available without a prescription from your practitioner or your health food store. Start with the dose and schedule recommended by your practitioner. (See: *How to Deal with Hormonal Imbalances and Fibroid Cysts)*

- Supplement your diet with a whey protein shake once or twice daily. Make sure you're eating plenty of protein, such as beef, chicken, turkey, fish, eggs, beans, nuts and seeds. Low protein stores can lead to low thyroid function, and so many ultra-sensitives are protein deficient.
- Eat plenty of iodine-containing foods, including mushrooms, garlic, onions, seafood, fish, and sea greens, but only if you are not allergic to them. Don't overindulge on thyroid blocking foods like cabbage, soy products, and peanuts.
- Get tested for food allergies using applied kinesiology. Food allergies can stir up the immune system which can quickly throw the thyroid out of balance. Thyroid dysfunction and most other organ imbalances can easily be traced back to an autoimmune reaction often created by the foods and beverages you consume.
- Supplement with organic iodine as needed. Low iodine levels from nutritional, genetic, or other causes will lead to low or even *high* thyroid function. Get guidance from your holistic practitioner to make sure your dose is carefully determined, and to make sure there are no conflicts with any other health issues.
- Correct low adrenal function. The thyroid gland relies on signals from the adrenal glands to function properly. It's all connected. Take a B complex 50 to 100mg daily with food, vitamin C with the bioflavonoids 500 to 1000mg two to three times daily, and panthothenic acid 500mg two to three times daily to keep your adrenals at top performance. You should begin to notice an overall energy improvement within a week or so.

Sensitive's summary:

All of the body's organs are interconnected. *All facets of life* are interconnected. *All of us* are interconnected. So it holds true in each situation: If you correct the right things that are out of balance the rest will fall into place.

How to manage

Asthma

We all need to breathe. Yet many ultra-sensitives have difficulty with this basic life-sustaining process, and this is especially true with the condition known as asthma. Asthma in the ultra-sensitive tends to start at a young age and continues to rear its ugly head all the way through the adult years. It's a curious thing, however, that so many young asthma sufferers are ultra-sensitive. Sure, less-sensitives can develop asthma too. But the *reasons* breathing problems occur in the ultra-sensitive are quite different than for the others.

Many ultra-sensitives are acutely tuned in to and aware of their soul purpose; they can still see and feel spirits and other energies, especially from birth until age seven or so. They can see everything clearly because the veil is still quite thin at that age and they have not yet succumbed to the full spectrum of energies and influences of the planet. However, once these ultra-sensitives have taken a gander at how challenging life can be on schoolhouse Earth, some are not sure they want to stick around for it. And some don't. The ones that do tend to develop breathing problems and exquisite sensitivities to almost all environmental toxins. That's why so many ultra-sensitives have so many food allergies and other immune sensitivities. Welcome to the world of asthma.

Here's the fix:

- Start taking n-acetyl-cysteine (NAC) 900mg twice daily continuously. This will help loosen your chest, improve breathing, and help clear your body of debilitating toxins.
- Start taking fish oil 1000 to 2000mg twice daily with food. Fish oil reduces inflammation and helps calm the immune response that's creating the breathing problems.

- Take magnesium 200mg two or three times daily. Magnesium helps relax the bronchial muscles and relieve spasms so you can breathe easier.
- Enjoy drinking fenugreek tea, several cups daily, to help loosen phlegm and improve your respiration. It's not bad-tasting, either.
- Vitamin C with the bioflavonoids (especially quercetin) can be very helpful in improving lung function and warding off inflammation. Work up slowly to daily doses of 5000mg or more per day, in divided doses with food. Vitamin C also works well to help detoxify the lungs from tobacco smoke and other environmental toxins.
- Get moderate exercise as tolerated. Yes, you may have shortness of breath, but as you begin to slowly work your lungs, oxygen capacity and breathing can improve. Start slow and don't push, but stay with it as tolerated. Inspiration is a great thing, both for breathing and for the spiritual health of the ultra-sensitive. The act of breathing is truly the source of *all* inspiration, so breathe fully and deeply to stay connected to the higher realms.
- Get food allergy tested through applied kinesiology. Food allergies are one of the top unrecognized causes of asthma and other breathing and immune problems. You will definitely be surprised to discover what you're allergic to. Stop consuming the identified culprits and your immune system will calm and your breathing will begin to improve.
- An environmental allergy panel can help you detect and avoid all of your environmental allergies. And you have many. Avoid or remove the culprits and you will breathe better and feel better. This can be performed accurately through kinesiology by a qualified holistic practitioner.
- Make sure you clear environmental allergies from the trees, grasses, and shrubs that grow in your area. These seasonal or year-round allergens can easily trigger and sustain asthmatic symptoms. Start taking vitamin C as recommended above, or any one of a number of natural antihistamine combination products available at the health food store or your practitioner's office. A liquid homeopathic blend of the antigenic antidotes for the allergens that grow in your area is also available and works extremely well for many people. Other supplements can also be helpful. Check with your practitioner.

- Stay clear of dairy products. They create mucus and make breathing more difficult. Ditto for wheat. Ninety percent of the population at large is allergic to these two common foodstuffs.
- Get a complete chakra and energy balancing session from your qualified energy worker, to help open your heart chakra. This is the chakra where the lungs reside. The opening and clearing of this chakra (and the others) will often help improve breathing, and more.
- Many ultra-sensitives experience breathing problems from birth, usually due to a subconscious apprehension about being in body. Still others have experienced past-life trauma, from choking or drowning or other physical or emotional events, creating breathing problems in the current life. The cellular memory from these traumas often results in environmental sensitivities and asthma. When done correctly, a regression session by a qualified practitioner will often improve breathing. Tune in. If you feel like you're harboring such traumas, get a clearing promptly.
- Get off the fence. Make the conscious commitment to yourself and to others that you do want to stick around. This acknowledgment alone can be enough to improve your breathing challenges. We need you. The planet needs you. Let's all breathe together.

Sensitive's summary:

Breathing is mandatory for the beings on this planet at this time. Yes, asthma and other breathing disorders can severely hamper the productivity and pleasure in life, but natural solutions are available to help the ultra-sensitives, and the others, get true inspiration.

How to manage

Gallbladder Problems

Ultra-sensitives tend to have more gallbladder symptoms than others. What else is new? Gallbladder problems are a gastrointestinal nemesis for millions of people, ultra-sensitive or not, across the globe. Nagging right-upper-quadrant pain, gas, heartburn, even fever and shoulder blade pain are just the beginning.

A clogged and inflamed gallbladder can also result in long-standing depression. That's right, *depression*. You've heard the term "melancholy." It's an old descriptor of low mood, or depression. And for good reason. Melancholy literally translates as "black bile," the color that bile can turn when gallbladder issues exist.

Ultra-sensitives are more prone to gallbladder problems because we tend to repress our angst and frustration rather than expressing it appropriately. You've heard the term "the gall of him." Translated, it means, "the NERVE of him (or her)," essentially an expression of anger and resentment. Held in long enough, anger and resentment will begin to generate little balls of cholesterol, bilirubin, and other substances that can clog the bile ducts, leading to the pain and inflammation. Left undetected, this condition can necessitate a visit to the emergency room, after which a surgeon may snatch that gallbladder away.

Here's the fix:

- Drink two to three glasses of organic unfiltered apple juice every day. Apples contain malic acid, which helps break down stones so that they can be eliminated from the body. If you're diabetic or tend toward severe hypoglycemia, take malic acid capsules instead of juice, as directed.

- Take magnesium 200mg once or twice daily, or more. If bowel cramping or loose stools begin to occur, back down the dose by one half and maintain it there. Magnesium can help prevent the formation of stones and also enhance their elimination.
- Take one tablespoonful of apple cider vinegar in four ounces of water, twice daily before meals. This will help keep your body alkaline, improve digestion, reduce acid reflux, and help dissolve gallstones.
- Take a broad-spectrum digestive enzyme halfway through two or three of your larger meals each day. Breaking down the fats, proteins, carbohydrates, and other nutrients more efficiently will help take the load off your gallbladder and the rest of your digestive tract. There are several digestive enzyme formulations available specifically for gallbladder imbalances.
- Drink at least ten to twelve glasses of distilled water each day to help flush out toxins and to keep you fully hydrated.
- Do ease back on the fatty foods and oils, even things like flax seed and olive oil, just for a few weeks or so. Give your gallbladder a rest.
- Perform a gallbladder cleanse ASAP, and then again about every year or two. As we age we tend to accumulate gallstones from diet, stress, and repressed angst. You'll digest your foods and your life better, and you'll feel better, after a cleanse. Remember, the gallstones are indeed in there, *even if they can't be detected through the usual diagnostic methods.* There are many gallbladder flush protocols available on the Internet, but it might be best to consider the one recommended by your holistic practitioner.
- If you're overweight, make diligent efforts to get your weight balanced. Many people with gallbladder symptoms have weight issues.
- Release all grudges now. That's right. NOW. Don't hold on to anger and resentment. And by all means, do learn to go with the flow. I mean it! Your gallbladder will thank you and you will feel better.
- If you harbor feelings of anger, guilt, resentment, shame, or any other negative emotion (and who hasn't had some of those from time to time?) consider a regression or emotional clearing session with a qualified holistic practitioner. This can help release the angst and help subdue gallbladder discomfort.

Take all steps possible to preserve your gallbladder. Removing the gallbladder should be a last resort, because a life without your gallbladder typically results in life-long digestive discomfort and inconvenience.

Sensitive's summary:

Gallbladder problems have become a pandemic in our society, and ultra-sensitives are especially susceptible. Got angst? Get rid of it!

How to manage

Insomnia

When you're a beacon of light, it's hard to get sleep. When you're a reservoir of sensitive energy, it's hard to get sleep. When you feel every little planetary and astrological shift, it's hard to get sleep. When you feel everybody's everything, it's hard to get sleep. Is it any wonder then that most ultra-sensitives have problems with sleep? No. It makes perfect sense, actually. We're the ones who can feel the pea a dozen mattresses below us. It's who we are.

There are some ultra-sensitives who will say, "Wait a minute. I sleep too much, and I can't get up." That may be the case. But the reason you sleep so much is because you're never really getting REM sleep, and your body is never really getting the rest and recovery it needs. In fact, your body is probably chronically exhausted from long-term sleep deprivation. What's a sensitive to do?

Here's the fix:

- Observe healthy sleep hygiene. Avoid daytime napping. Go to bed at the same time each night. Avoid exercise and food consumption (especially heavy meat proteins) and excess fluids within three hours of bedtime.
- Make sure your sleeping room and your home are free of clutter, tidy and organized. Clutter is a toxin, and through an as-of-yet unexplained subconscious mechanism it can actually keep you awake, even if you're trying to sleep in a hotel room halfway around the world. Try it yourself. Clear your clutter in your house, especially in your sleep room, and then keep a sleep diary to see how you respond.
- Remove all unnecessary electrics from the sleeping room. This includes computers, cell phones, radios, video game-boxes, and the like. If your TV must stay, make sure you cover it with a towel each

night before bed. That will protect you from exposure to the EMF it emits, even while it's off. Even an LED clock readout glaring your way can be enough to keep you awake.

- Make sure the room is dark. Use light-blocking shades over window coverings to accomplish this.
- Practice nose breathing, not mouth breathing, when you lie down to sleep. This will increase oxygenation, relax you, and help you get to sleep.
- Make sure the room temperature is comfortable. Many ultra-sensitives cannot tolerate air conditioners or heaters running at night.
- Do NOT use an electric blanket to keep yourself warm at night. You are electric, and very sensitive to electrical currents. Electric blankets can disrupt your aura, your immune system, and your sleep patterns and can actually be detrimental to your health. Instead, use a heavier blanket or multiple layers of non-electrified blankets.
- Make sure there are no mirrors in the sleeping room. Mirrors stir up energies and can facilitate the entry of unwanted spirit activity. Mirrors are a sure way to keep yourself tossing and turning each night. Cover them or get rid of them.
- Avoid or minimize the use of prescription drugs to get sleep. These only mask the causes of insomnia, and they can disrupt your intuitive gifts, and ultra-sensitives (as well as less-sensitives) can easily develop life-long dependence on them.
- Instead: Start taking inositol. Inositol is a non-addictive and inexpensive B vitamin, is effective for any age, and there are no side effects or drug interactions to worry about. Take 500mg to 1000mg twenty minutes before you want to go to sleep.
- There are many other natural sleep aids that can also help, including many in combination formulas like GABA, valerian, chamomile, passion flower, melatonin, skullcap, and seditol. Check with your local holistic practitioner to see what's best for you.
- Never go to bed angry. Harboring subconscious anger or even bubbling conscious anger is a sure-fire way to keep you tossing and turning all night. Whatever it is, make peace with it before you go to bed.
- Last, and *absolutely not least*, make sure you've cleared or resolved all your emotional issues, such as unbalanced relationships, financial woes, unacceptable employment situations, etc. An emotional

clearing session with your holistic practitioner can help resolve these issues and restore your natural, healthy sleeping skills. Trust me. They're in there.

Sensitive's summary:

Getting six to nine hours of quality REM sleep each night is mandatory for good health, especially for the ultra-sensitive. You need to be truly rested to do the work you came here to do.

How to manage

Anemia

Because of our high-frequency existence, we ultra-sensitives tend to burn through our energy banks very quickly each day, and much more rapidly than most less-sensitives. When you add that intense energy expenditure to an already ultra-sensitive immune system (which governs the blood system and almost everything else in our bodies) and take into account the often-poor nutrition status of many ultra-sensitives, the result is often anemia, a low red blood cell count. In fact, anemia is a common affliction among ultra-sensitives everywhere.

If you suffer from chronic fatigue, breathing problems, low mood, and pale skin coloring, there's a good chance you have iron-poor blood, or what is called anemia.

Here's the fix:

- Ground yourself. Start by eating more red meat. Red meat is not only a great source of natural iron, it is grounding. Another way to ground yourself is to spend several minutes daily on all fours in the dirt. That's right, in the dirt on all fours. This is a great way to discharge excess energy into Mother Earth and can help you feel more energized and more balanced. You can also perform your choice of healing mantras to help keep your powerful energies balanced and grounded. No matter which way you choose, grounding can help keep those bubbling internal energies from creating health problems, and from draining your iron stores.
- Protect yourself, or remove yourself from the common energy zappers: negative people, high stress situations and relationships, and electric devices such as cell towers, cell phones, and computers. You should also consider using EMF deflectors on these devices, available inexpensively in town or on the Internet. You can also protect

yourself by carrying dark stones on your person. (See Part I: *You Are an Empath*)

- Eat more protein, including red meat, chicken, turkey, beans, eggs, fish, and nuts and seeds. Whatever you do, don't skip meals. You need your nourishment, now more than ever. If you suffer from acid reflux or other digestive symptoms, there's a good chance you're not absorbing your nutrients. Over time this can lead to anemia. The answer?
- Use a high potency digestive enzyme complex halfway through two or three of your meals each day to improve digestion and nutrient absorption. Apple cider vinegar, one tablespoonful in water twice daily before food, can also be helpful in that regard.
- Include plenty of beets, brown rice, almonds, spinach and other dark green vegetables in your diet to help bolster your iron levels naturally.
- Start taking an iron supplement every day with food, as directed by your practitioner. Take vitamin C 500mg with every dose of iron to improve iron absorption into your system. Please note that iron supplementation should be done cautiously, if at all, when there is a history of heart disease, arthritis, or a cancer risk. Get guidance if you're not sure.
- Take methylcobalamin (activated vitamin B12) l000mcg under your tongue twice daily. B12 is crucial to the blood building process. Remember, swallowing B12 deactivates it. Use only the sublingual (under the tongue) formulations if you want results.
- Take a B complex 50 to 100mg, with breakfast or lunch every day. The B vitamins are very much involved in the blood-building process and are necessary to restore iron stores. The B vitamins will also help strengthen your adrenal glands and calm your tender nervous system.
- Get plenty of rest. Make sure you're getting at least seven hours of uninterrupted REM sleep nightly to help your body rest and regenerate. That way it can have the energy necessary to process and retain the nutrients it needs.
- Avoid life's dramas as much as possible. That means removing yourself from uncomfortable or stressful situations whenever possible. Long term stress and the resulting acid reflux can eventually create bleeding ulcers and anemia. We certainly don't need that.
- Avoid the regular use of over-the-counter and prescription NSAIDS (non-steroidal anti-inflammatory drugs) such as aspirin, ibuprofen,

and naproxen. Excess use of these common painkillers can create bleeding problems and commonly results in anemia without your even realizing that it's happening. If you are taking prescription blood thinners like Plavix or Coumadin, or any other prescription, make sure that these are not causing unseen or "silent" bleeding. Even natural medicines like fish or flax oil, curcumin, boswellia, ginger, and garlic can thin the blood and result in silent bleeding, especially in combination with any of the above. Consult with your holistic practitioner to rule out any of the above agents as anemia-inducing suspects.

If your low energy and anemia persists despite taking reasonable steps as listed above, consult with your healthcare practitioner to rule out any other issues.

Sensitive's summary:

When an ultra-sensitive is pitted against the harshness of the planetary energies and challenges of our time, the resultant exhaustion from anemia is a real issue that deserves immediate attention. Clear the culprits and replenish the nutrients, and your blood count and your energy will improve.

How to manage

Weight Issues

Weight issues are the Achilles Heel of today's society. People everywhere, and especially women, seem to be constantly looking for ways to lose weight. It's a never-ending battle to achieve that magical weight balance. But it's not just weight *loss* people are seeking help with. For many people, especially ultra-sensitives, its weight *gain.* Keeping weight ON is an issue because ultra-sensitives burn through so much energy and so many calories by their mere existence.

Yes, it's true. Keeping the weight on is the world's *other* weight issue. Let's consider how to deal with weight issues of both kinds.

Here's the fix:

- Balance your hormones. Low progesterone levels eventually lead to low thyroid hormone production and function. What's more, low progesterone levels are often accompanied by high estrogen levels. This combination of low progesterone and high estrogen classically lead to weight gain. That means you could exercise 24/7 and eat like a bird and you still wouldn't lose a pound, until you corrected your hormone levels. Have yours checked by a holistic practitioner, and then supplement with topical progesterone cream as directed.
- Balance your thyroid function. Low thyroid function is a common culprit in weight gain. It's important to understand that thyroid blood tests are often inaccurate, so have your thyroid levels checked by your holistic practitioner using applied kinesiology. When done correctly, these results are extremely accurate and quickly available.
- Many people who take thyroid prescription medicines like levothyroxine or Armour thyroid end up in a *hyper*thyroid state. And being hyperthyroid can also cause weight gain, because the thyroid is functioning inefficiently. If you're taking thyroid medication and are

still having issues with excess weight, or if you're unable to put on weight, work with your holistic practitioner to get things balanced once and for all.

- If you're craving carbohydrates, sugars, sweets, or any foods for that matter, start taking chromium picolinate 200mcg two or three times daily before meals. Also, add the blue green algae known as spirulina, to your diet. Start with two tablets before breakfast and two before lunch. This will help balance blood sugars and help curb those nagging food cravings.
- There are many other supplements out there that contain ingredients designed to curb appetite and improve metabolism. Some can be effective, but *only* if thyroid and the sex hormones are balanced first. By all means, avoid any and all stimulant supplements such as guarana, caffeine, and bitter orange. These can throw your sensitive immune system and metabolism into orbit and create new health problems. Just say no.
- Clear your emotional hurt *now.* Unresolved emotional hurt will eventually, if not immediately, result in emotional eating, which almost uniformly results in weight gain. That's because unresolved emotional hurt triggers a cascade of events that cause the body to add weight in an attempt to protect itself. Break the cycle once and for all. Have an emotional clearing session or a regression session performed by a qualified practitioner.
- Correct insomnia. Insomnia raises cortisol levels which cause blood sugar swings and increases cravings for all foods. Even one night of poor sleep can make you ravenous the next day. The reality is that many people with excess-weight issues also have chronic sleep problems. It's all connected. Correct your sleeping habits today. (See: *How to Manage Insomnia*)
- Don't skip meals. This just makes things worse. Instead, eat three to six smaller meals a day, each containing some form of protein, such as beef, chicken, turkey, fish, beans, eggs, vegetables, or nuts and seeds.
- Avoid caffeine, aspartame and all artificial sweeteners. These can actually cause weight *gain* and other health problems over time. Use only stevia or other natural sweeteners.
- Avoid all fad diets. Fad diets most often result in the return of weight problems and often other metabolic imbalances. Remember, no type

of food modification diet will work unless and until you correct your metabolism, emotions, and other lifestyle factors.

- Clear or resolve stressful or unbalanced relationships or routines in your life, including uncomfortable job situations. Raging cortisol levels from any of life's stressors can play havoc on blood sugars, food cravings, and your metabolic organs, resulting in weight gain and other metabolic problems.
- Avoid over-exercising. Too much exercise can drain your adrenal glands, which will cycle back to cause low thyroid function. This can create a vicious and frustrating cycle of weight gain. Exercise only in moderation.
- Be realistic about weight loss expectations. You should lose no more than one to two pounds per week. Anything faster than that and the weight will come back with a vengeance.
- Some people, and especially ultra-sensitives, have low iodine levels in their systems as a result of poor nutrition, genetic factors, or more. Supplementation with iodine may be necessary to help your body produce more active thyroid hormone. Your practitioner is best suited to help you get back in balance safely.
- **If you can't keep the weight ON,** drink a whey protein shake once or twice daily in addition to your regular meals. Add a concentrated liquid protein supplement to each shake as directed. Start taking chromium picolinate 200mcg twice daily to balance blood sugars, and B complex 100mg daily to balance appetite. Don't skip meals. Rather, eat five to six smaller meals daily, and whenever you're hungry. If you're taking prescription medicines, especially thyroid medicines, or if you continue to lose weight, consult with your practitioner promptly. There may be another underlying issue that needs attention.

Weight loss is a hot button for many people on this Planet. Ultra-sensitives are no exception. There are many people and places touting the benefits of their weight management program. Be discerning. Most do not correct the underlying cause, and eventually the weight will return. Use your intuition. You'll know what to do.

Sensitive's summary:

You have a sensitive metabolic system and therefore are more readily subject to weight variations than most. Just pay attention to what your body is trying to tell you and then you'll weigh exactly what your body is designed to weigh.

How to manage

Oral Hygiene

This may sound like a trite issue, and maybe even one that makes you a bit squeamish, but the lack of proper oral hygiene can have serious health consequences, especially for the ultra-sensitive. It's an area of health that is largely overlooked by a majority of the population, yet taking simple daily steps to address it can have profoundly positive impact on your health. And who couldn't use that?

I have found that about a third of my patients carry an identifiable bacterial load, mostly as a result of poor dental hygiene, that is, neglecting to regularly brush and floss. Oral bacteria left unchecked can lead to heart disease, autoimmune disorders, and poor health, not to mention offensive breath. And for ultra-sensitives with hair trigger immune systems, getting bacterial loads under control is essential to our longevity.

Here's the fix:

- Start flossing. If you've never flossed before, today is a great day to start. There are certain techniques to perform this important task correctly. Rather than discuss the finer points of technique, I recommend that you speak with your dental professional or check the Internet for guidance. If you've never flossed before, your gums will be very tender when you start and may even bleed a bit. Be gentle. The bleeding and tenderness will diminish as you begin to floss regularly.
- Brush your teeth at least twice daily, after breakfast and after your last meal of the day. Always brush *after* flossing is complete. Your teeth will feel and look better, and you'll get to keep them in your mouth longer. Choose a natural toothpaste that does NOT contain fluoride or other nasty ingredients. Beware; the use of fluoride on a regular basis

actually *causes* brittle bones, not the opposite. Stay clear of it in all forms.

- Gargle with hydrogen peroxide on a regular basis. This is especially important if you feel like you have a lingering or simmering dental or oral infection. Dilute the peroxide with an equal amount of water, swish it around for thirty seconds, and then spit it out. You can repeat this up to twice daily to maintain tip-top oral hygiene.
- If your gums or teeth are not in good repair, visit with your dental professional. Don't ignore dental pain, swelling, mouth sores, or unexplained mouth bleeding. Unattended, these can lead to chronic and debilitating health problems in the ultra-sensitive, and in others.

Sensitive's summary:

Good dental hygiene is a requirement for keeping your sensitive immune system in balance. If dental hygiene has taken a backseat to your chronic health problems, bring it to the top of your attention list and make it a daily routine. When it comes to good oral hygiene, it's never too late to start.

How to manage

Porous Bones

Ultra-sensitives have porous energy. That is, our energy is light, gentle, and fragile and can be easily disrupted. This porous energy permeates and bathes the rest of our bodies, our entire internal make-up, including the bony structure we know as our skeleton. As a result, ultra-sensitives are prone to develop bone density issues, the condition known as osteoporosis, which literally translates as "porous bones." And as it turns out, the more sensitive you are, the greater the potential for low bone-density. It's just the way it is.

The medical community at large has made a big "to do" about the dangers of brittle bones and the risk of bone fractures in older people, primarily of the female gender. Sure, it's an important area of health that needs to be addressed, but much of the hype seems to be related to their efforts to sell expensive and toxic drugs to treat it. But bone loss in the ultra-sensitive and others can be handled just fine, thank you, using simple, natural means.

Here's the fix:

- Avoid drinking cow's milk and eating cheese and other dairy products just for the purpose of acquiring food-based calcium. Most people, and especially ultra-sensitives, are allergic to these foods so consume them only occasionally and only for the pleasure of eating them. If you're searching for healthy food-based calcium:
- Eat plenty of green leafy vegetables on a regular basis, including broccoli, parsley, kale, and spinach. Almonds, tofu, and dried figs are among the many other non-dairy foods high in calcium. And there are plenty of them. Enjoy these as often as you wish, and on a regular basis.
- Supplement with 2000 units of vitamin D daily with breakfast. This will help stabilize your bone structure and your sensitive immune system.

- Take calcium citrate 300 to 400mg twice daily with meals. This is enough for most people. Although higher doses have been advocated in the past, they are no longer necessary in most cases. Add magnesium 150 to 200mg twice daily, or more, to complement the calcium absorption. Despite popular thinking, calcium and magnesium can be taken at the same time.
- Drink a soy protein shake once or twice daily, if you're not allergic to soy products. Soy can help raise bone density and provide the additional protein your body needs to stay fit. A derivative of the isoflavones found in soy, called ipriflavone, has also been shown to help maintain and improve bone density and can safely be used along with calcium, magnesium, and other natural bone density supporting agents. Start with 300 to 600mg daily with food and stay with it.
- Vitamin K2, known as menaquinone-7, at doses of 100mg daily can be added to improve bone density when other natural methods are not enough. Take it with your breakfast meal.
- There are many other supplements and bone formulas available that contain products that can help improve your bone density, such as silica, horsetail, copper, boron, and manganese. These can all be helpful, but you may choose to get some guidance to help find the right combination for you.
- Easy on caffeine. Caffeine has been shown to leach calcium from the bones. Ditto for sodas that contain phosphoric acid (and many of them do). Stay clear of these.
- Walk thirty to forty-five minutes every day, but avoid power walking. It's not necessary and can actually subvert the attempt to maintain bone density. You are sensitive, so no extremes.
- Minimize your exposure to fluorescent lights, computers, high power lines, and other electromagnetic emitting devices. These can drain your immune system and lead to bone porosity. Remember, you are electric; therefore exposure to other electric fields over time can easily drain yours.
- Stay clear of negative people, unhealthy relationships, and stressful situations. These subtle and not so subtle energies can disrupt your sensitive energy fields and reduce bone density. Protect yourself from these energy vampires by keeping dark stones on your person. Hematite, black onyx, and black tourmaline are good choices. They

absorb harmful negative energies so you don't. Clear them nightly under running water, or outside in the moonlight.

- Millions of women and men, including many ultra-sensitives, are unnecessarily taking Synthroid or the generic levothyroxine to boost their thyroid function. Thyroid imbalances are almost always due to secondary undetected and uncorrected underlying problems, usually low progesterone levels or low adrenal function. Complicating matters even further is the fact that the blood tests used to determine thyroid function are often inaccurate, leading to the inappropriate use of these agents. This can actually create new health problems, including osteoporosis.

Yes, Synthroid, or levothyroxine, is well known to cause osteoporosis. If you're taking this medication and have been diagnosed with low bone density, discuss this matter promptly with your practitioner and make every effort to taper off the medication with guidance, as soon as possible. If you need assistance, reach my office.

Sensitive's summary:

Low bone density is common among ultra-sensitive women and men. Fortunately, it can easily be remedied through natural means without the need for toxic prescription drugs.

How to manage

Environmental Toxicity

We live on a polluted planet, a planet filled with toxins--in the water, in the air, in our food supply, and in our everyday environment. Heavy metals, chemicals, industrial byproducts, prescription medicines, food additives, they're out there. And they can wreak havoc on the unsuspecting and vulnerable ultra-sensitives.

It's a constant battle; a war between our physical and emotional bodies and the environment we live in and around. Ultra-sensitives have an exceptionally difficult time coping with these toxins and tend to experience organ imbalances more often than others, and to have more severe repercussions. Chronic fatigue syndrome (CFIDS), Lupus, rheumatoid arthritis, asthma, headaches, depression, anxiety, insomnia, skin reactions-- these are just a few of the health challenges that can be traced back in one form or another to the toxins within our body. It's time to get rid of them.

Here's the fix:

- Take 1/4 to 1/2 packet of chlorella powder in a glass of water before breakfast daily. This will initiate a gradual detoxification of heavy metals such as mercury, cadmium, lead, and other environmental toxins.
- Detoxify your liver, lungs, and your entire body by starting on n-acetyl-cysteine, or NAC, 900mg twice daily continuously. Cleansing and strengthening these elimination organs is the key to a successful detoxification program.
- Clear your lymph system with tincture of burdock. Follow the directions on the bottle and take it for at least thirty days to help your lymph system mobilize and clear unhealthy waste products.
- There are many other herbal detoxification formulas on the market that can help you accomplish a successful detoxification. Choose

them carefully and with professional guidance. Regardless which product or products you choose, be prepared to experience the symptoms of detoxification. These may include flu-like symptoms, muscle aches and pains, headaches, digestive discomfort including diarrhea, and skin rashes. Make certain you are properly nourished before you commence a detoxification program of any kind.

- Consume whey protein shakes, one full serving once to twice daily, in addition to your regular meals. Whey is a great detoxifier and can help balance your immune system, your blood sugars, and provide the nourishment you're going to need when you begin the process.
- Drink at least ten to twelve large glasses of distilled water during your detox, and on a regular basis, to flush out toxins and keep your body "fluid."
- High colonics performed by a qualified colonic therapist can be helpful in clearing away the accumulated gunk hiding in the nooks and crannies of the digestive tract. Over time these waste products can contribute to many health maladies, including muscle aches and pains, immune problems, digestive problems, even cancer.
- Get an ionic foot detoxification bath. This is a water and salt detoxification footbath powered by a low level current that stimulates the removal of heavy metals and other toxins through the pores on the bottoms of your feet. It also initiates a gentle detoxification of all your internal elimination organs. Some holistic practitioners offer these services, or you may purchase your own foot detox bath machine.
- Become ultra-diligent about the types of foods you consume and the types of products you put on your body, including lip balms, toothpaste, cosmetics, shampoo, detergents, everything. Use and consume only products that contain natural ingredients.
- Maintain a positive attitude about life and your role on the planet. A positive attitude helps you and the cells in your body become filters of toxicities rather than a repository. It really does work. Start today.
- Remember that festering negative emotions like fear, anger, resentment, guilt, and shame are also powerful toxins to your internal environment. Work with a qualified holistic practitioner to help clear *all* that you're holding onto on the inside. You will feel better.
- Read my book *Extreme Clearing for Perfect Health* to learn more about how to clear ALL of life's toxins. You'll be surprised at what you've overlooked.

If you're uncertain about how to begin your detoxification program, or would prefer to have someone guide you, work with your holistic practitioner to set up a program tailored to your specific health needs and symptoms.

Sensitive's summary:

We are all toxic. But not everyone is as sensitive as you. Honor that by becoming aware of all the things in your life that are making you toxic, and work to stay clear of them.

How to manage

The Aging Process

We are all going through our biological progression. We don't just age. We change. We change physically, emotionally, mentally, and certainly spiritually as the three dimensional time clock clicks on. Understanding and coping with these energetic and biological changes can be quite challenging, even disheartening, unless and until we accept them as a necessary part of our journey.

As ultra-sensitives, we experience progressive changes in our thinking abilities, our joints and mobility, our sleep patterns, even our physical and emotional energy levels, and often at a more accelerated rate than others. Changes in hearing, vision, and other senses can occur literally overnight in some cases.

But all is not lost. As we lose the acuity of some senses, we often begin to activate our *esoteric senses*, especially our "sixth sense." It's part of the ultra-sensitive aging process and the cycles of life. But you can learn to age gracefully and with dignity, and with all of your faculties intact and vibrant.

Here's the fix:

- Start paying attention to new sensations that are sneaking up on you, like the ability to see or feel lights, or sense the presence of energies. These new gifts are presented to you to balance the changes occurring in the other five senses, and they are here to help escort you through the next steps in your life path.
- Start taking resveratrol or red wine capsules on a daily basis. These are powerful healing antioxidants to help keep your blood vessels and other body parts healthier, longer. If you choose and can tolerate it, regular red wine consumption, one or two 4 ounce glasses nightly, can be equally beneficial.

- Supplementation with vitamins C and E and other natural antioxidant vitamins can help extend your longevity. Work with your practitioner to develop an anti-aging regimen designed specifically for you.
- Stay positive. Positive thinking breeds positive health. Negative thinking breeds negative health, and can reduce our longevity. And you get to choose how you wish to think. Don't like the mental tape that's been playing in your life? Make a new one. It's not hard to do. Confer with your holistic practitioner for more guidance.
- Be jolly. Laugh out loud, sing, dance, and love like there's no tomorrow. That'll help make sure there is one.
- Keep an open heart. Forgive those who you believe have wronged you, and move on. Remember, what you hold onto will make you sick, and make you old, fast. Just get rid of it.
- Got emotional baggage? We all do. We've all been through a lot in this life, and perhaps many other lives. Get rid of it. Consider an emotional clearing session or past life regression with a qualified practitioner. You're likely to live longer and you'll be happier.
- Stay clear of unnatural cosmetics and body care products. Read labels carefully, and remember, whatever you put on your body will get into your body. Be discerning and choose your healthcare products wisely.
- Maintain a healthy diet. That doesn't necessarily mean you must become a vegan. That's a personal choice. Instead, be particular about what types of foods and food additives you place in your sacred temple, your body. For starters, stay clear of aspartame, saccharin, margarine, high fructose corn syrup, MSG, modified corn starch, modified *anything*, and anything labeled only as "natural flavors." Just say no. Read my book *Extreme Clearing for Perfect Health* for more guidance.
- Drink at least ten to twelve glasses of distilled or purified water every day to flush out toxins and keep your organs vital and your body well hydrated.
- Do what you love, and not what you don't. That may mean making wholesale changes in your career choices or lifestyle. But it's worth it, because you'll live longer and be happier. Trust what you feel, and allow your intuition to help you age joyfully and gracefully.

You're not alone. Everyone is aging. But you can make your journey a healthier and more pleasant one simply by staying young at heart and young in thought. It's true. You're only as old as you feel. So feel young, be young, and live young.

Sensitive's summary:

Whatever your life choices are, remember this: We came into this life to experience joy. When we deprive ourselves of joy to the point of unhappiness and dissatisfaction, we tend to age more quickly, and we can shorten our life span. If drinking wine and smoking cigarettes truly gives you joy, you are likely to outlive those who have chronically deprived themselves of all the things they love.

How to manage

Pent-up Anger

We are ultra-sensitive, but we're not all necessarily saints 24/7. So, like the rest of the inhabitants of the planet, many of us can become angry with certain people, certain situations or events, and, in many cases, even our own challenging life plight (See Part I: *Why Am I Here, Really?*) After all, being an ultra-sensitive on a mission isn't necessarily a bowl of cherries.

The liver is the depot for anger and resentment, and by now yours is likely overflowing. When we hold onto enough anger or resentment over time, we're bound to develop a congested liver. When the liver becomes congested with these energy toxins, cholesterol levels can rise, and we can become fatigued or depressed (and even more angry, in a vicious cycle), experience digestive imbalances, and more.

Here's the fix:

- Become a filter, *not* a depository. That is, dirty energy in, process it, then clean energy out. Let the angst run through you, not *into you.* This can take some conscious practice, but its well worth the effort. Just start becoming aware of how you process and filter all the energies in your life. Make it part of your daily routine.
- Don't sweat the small stuff. The small stuff is the stuff that has nothing to do with your path, such as your nine-to-five job, that big house, or that sagging bank account. The big stuff is being able to get up in the morning and have the ability to create your own reality. Become grateful for that.
- Find a healthy outlet for your anger. Regular exercise, like walking or running, or playing sports or some other physical activity, are safe ways to release the angst.
- Channel these pent-up energies into some of your favorite hobbies. Become more right-brained, more creative, so that you can transmute

the negativity into positivity. Start writing, singing, dancing…expressing. This will help you process the angst into something useful for you and the planet.

- Stand or sit down in the dirt or the grass for several minutes every day, either in your backyard or in a place in nature that makes you feel relaxed. This will allow any excess angst and energy to drain into the earth and release the pent-up energy you're carrying. This type of energy discharging is safe, effective, and quite pleasurable. And you get to enjoy the peaceful energies of nature.
- Take your inositol!
- If you catch yourself becoming upset with someone or something, speak up. Don't be malicious or condescending, or have mal intent, but do speak up. Do it for *your* health, not theirs. Expressing yourself by speaking up will help them learn the lesson from the event, and it will help you release what could be making you sick.
- Start taking milk thistle daily as directed on the package. This will help rebuild liver cells and help clear physical and energetic toxins that you have accumulated.
- Take a B complex 50 to 100mg every day with breakfast. This will help strengthen your liver, adrenal glands, and your sensitive nervous system, which has been ravaged by angst.
- Get an emotional clearing or regression session from a qualified healthcare practitioner. In many cases, today's anger is from yesterday's (or past life) event or trauma. Get rid of it. It's keeping you from joy, wellbeing, and your path.
- See every, and I mean every life challenge, every potential anger trigger as a gift, an opportunity to learn something about yourself and others. See it as an opportunity to grow and evolve. That way you won't get angry about it, you'll be grateful for it.
- Make amends. Right now! Forgive them. Forgive all those that you believe have wronged you in some way. Do it for *your* good, not theirs. Make sure it's a heartfelt and complete release. If you begin to weep, you've got it done. Congratulations! You just made your liver and the rest of your organs very happy!

Sensitive's summary:

Remember, what you hold on to will eventually make you sick. So get rid of the angst and be well.

How to manage

Bug Bites

Now this may sound like no big deal to most people. But let me tell you; when you are an ultra-sensitive, your immune system is easily disturbed and rattled, even from a simple bug bite. And I can tell you from personal experience that a spider bite, or some other kind of bug bite, can ruin a perfectly good day, maybe even a week. Why? Because a simple bug bite can throw the ultra-sensitive's immune system into a tizzy, making you feel miserable for quite some time.

Perhaps you've been clawing at an itch without even realizing you were doing it. You may have absolutely no idea that you've even been bitten until, all of a sudden, you notice that your joints are starting to ache, you have more muscle or joint pain, you've got a headache that just won't quit, or you are experiencing sudden bouts of fatigue. If you think you've become a bug-bite victim, step in front of a mirror and **do the following:**

a) Admire your amazing body, no matter the shape or size.
b) Carefully examine your body, top to bottom, in all the nooks and crannies (seriously), for any raised, red areas or itchy areas where a bite may have occurred.

There it is, sure as day. A little entrance wound or pustule courtesy of an uninvited critter. What do you do now?

Here's the fix:

- Make sure your dogs, cats, and other pets are pest-free. Use a natural flea collar or solution to clear them, and to prevent further re-infection.

- Clear away cobwebs and other places that these pests may be hiding out. Vacuum and clean your home regularly to eliminate nests or trouble spots.
- If your mattress is more than five years old, make sure there are no bedbugs residing within. If there are any, it may be time for a new mattress. Bedbug infestations are becoming rampant across the country.
- Most rogue bites occur when you are sleeping, so wear jammie bottoms and do your best to cover any exposed skin areas before going to bed.
- If you live in mosquito country or have them seasonally, do whatever you need to dry up their breeding grounds, such as ponds and pools.
- Sure, you could spray, or get your place sprayed, with a pesticide. But make sure you or they use organic pesticide products. And remember that even the "organic" or "natural" pesticides can stir up immune problems in ultra-sensitives. Weigh the risks against the benefits, and make sure your pets are safe from pesticide exposure, too.
- Start taking thiamine, vitamin B1 100mg a day with food. This will help make your blood less desirable to these varmints, and you'll get fewer bites.
- Start taking chlorella powder or tablets 200 to 400mg daily before breakfast. This will help rid your body of the toxins more quickly.
- Take a dose of milk thistle once or twice daily to help your liver clear the toxins or venom left behind by these little buggers. You will find that many of your symptoms will resolve more quickly.
- Apply a dab of Rescue Remedy cream and maybe even some calendula, echinacea, or other natural topical antibacterial to the bites sites two or three times daily. This will help heal the wounds quickly. Over-the-counter Polysporin ointment is also safe to use.
- If the bite sites do not heal within a few days, or if they start to get red, hot, or discolored, visit with your healthcare practitioner promptly. You may require antibiotics, or more.

Sensitive's summary:

Spread the word to other ultra-sensitives. Most would never realize that bug bites might be a trigger for their autoimmune symptoms. It is real. It does happen. Now you know.

How to manage

The Jewelry Paradox

Many people love to wear jewelry. But for the ultra-sensitive, wearing jewelry can be a paradox. Wedding bands, earrings, or even piercing jewelry contain nickel, gold, silver, platinum, or other metallic substances that can cause allergic reactions in the ultra-sensitive. These reactions can be localized, at the location of the jewelry, or they can cause a generalized rash and immune response anywhere on your body.

For years I wore a high quality eighteen carat gold ring on my left hand. Then, out of the blue, one day years later, I began to develop a rash on that hand. Later in life, I wore a platinum wedding band for several years, until I developed a severe rash and chafing on that hand. Finally, I thought I had the problem licked. I found a simple sterling silver band that I seemed to tolerate well for a while. Several months later the rash returned. I just couldn't win.

Finally I realized that as an ultra-sensitive I could not wear any metallic jewelry without developing a reaction to one or more of the metals in it. These days, I am pleased to report that I can indeed wear an agate *stone* wedding band without developing an allergic reaction. What can your sensitive immune system tolerate?

If you've developed a rash on your body from jewelry, detergent, or *anything* you've put *on* it, **here's the fix:**

- Use hypoallergenic detergents and soaps at all times. This will minimize any reactions between your metallic jewelry and your sensitive skin and immune system.
- Make sure all products that you put on your body are free of unnatural ingredients. The rule of thumb: If you wouldn't put it in your mouth, don't put it *on* your body. This applies to lip balm, makeup, hair

coloring (use henna-based colors; no ammonia or peroxides), lotion, soap, detergent, toothpaste, mouthwash, you name it.

- If you react to metallic substances, consider wearing non-metallic jewelry when possible, made from stone, hemp or other materials.
- Start taking colostrum capsules as directed on the label. Colostrum is an immune stabilizer that can help minimize the effects of allergic reactions to jewelry, foods and other elements that so many ultra-sensitives are sensitive to.
- Fish oil can also help stabilize the immune response to metallics and other allergens. Start with 1000mg twice daily with food. If you take prescription blood thinners like Plavix or Coumadin, do get guidance before you start.
- Do a trial separation with your jewelry. See if your rash or other symptoms clear when you keep the jewelry off for at least one month. Another option is to take your jewelry off at night when you sleep. Keep close tabs on how you respond.
- If you have removed all jewelry from your person and your skin rashes persist, do a thorough and meticulous inventory of everything you wear on your body, including all topical products. Often, the causative allergen is the last one you'd expect, like your detergent or deodorant. Eliminate the likely suspects and your rash will likely clear.
- Eliminate systemic toxins. Systemic bowel infections such as parasites, candidiasis, and bacterium, as well as heavy metal toxicity are often the culprits behind jewelry reactions, and other allergic reactions. Work with your holistic practitioner to identify and clear these offenders. (See: *How to Manage Environmental Toxicity*) A detoxification of your system, which may include a colon cleanse or high colonics, may be all that is needed to remedy the jewelry paradox.

Jewelry is lovely, but for the ultra-sensitive it can sometimes be just another environmental toxin. If your sensitive immune system and your metallic jewelry don't get along, come up with other ways to make a special and unique statement about yourself. That way you can look good and feel good, all at the same time.

Sensitive's summary:

Sensitive people have sensitive immune systems. Honor the intent that the jewelry was designed to create, and you may choose not to wear any jewelry at all.

How to manage

Spirit Attachments

Ultra-sensitives carry a high frequency energy signal. It's part of our makeup. We're like a beacon of light. As such, we tend to attract non-physical energies and entities by the droves.

Essentially, ultra-sensitives are spirit magnets. And whether you believe in ghosts, or entities or whatever you choose to call them, or not, they know who you are and they know where you live. Perhaps you've seen things, heard things, experienced a spirit up close and personal. Maybe you hear knocks or cracks in the walls, or perhaps your household electronics and water features have been acting up. You may even get lucky and find a cryptic EVP (electronic voice phenomena) on your answering machine or other recording or broadcasting device, like I did.

Don't be alarmed. They can't hurt you, but they can become an annoyance and an energy drain, both physically and emotionally. Some ultra-sensitives can easily sense when these energies are about them, others just can't figure out why they feel so squirmy, apprehensive, angry, and depressed, or why they're waking up at 3 AM each morning. Well, now you know.

What are the symptoms of spirit attachments? Insomnia, especially between 2 AM and 4 AM, feelings of apprehension, anxiety or panic, nervousness, sudden or chronic mood changes, disorientation, dizziness, exhaustion, and sadness are some of the classic symptoms.

One of the first things I check for when a patient reports any of these symptoms is spirit attachments. Curiously, most ultra-sensitives are not really surprised to learn that they are indeed corded and *courted* by spirits, and many will even report about a passed-over loved one or a familiar spirit guide who visits frequently. Still others will panic and demand that the spirits be banished immediately.

Here's the fix:

- Have an entity clearing performed by an experienced and qualified energy worker. There are many people who claim to know how to do this, yet few actually do. Use your intuition, and get references. If you need help, contact my office.
- Perform a thorough evaluation of your living space. Find out if your home has been built over burial grounds or historic sites where people have perished. If so, you may have found the source of your spirit activity.
- Examine all the items in your house. Antique furnishings and nick-knacks often carry energies of passed-over loved ones or other spirits. Pay particular attention to old mirrors. These tend to act as a conduit for spirit activity. Make sure there are no mirrors in your sleeping area. Cover the ones you can. Get rid of the rest.
- Take a salt and soda bath before bedtime regularly, especially if you are a practicing healer, intuitive, or energy worker. Place ¼ cup each of baking soda and sea salt (non-iodized) in a tub of warm water. Soak from head to toe for fifteen to twenty minutes before you retire each night.
- Before you go to bed each night, *command* that all spirit activity cease for the night, and insist that they leave you alone. The exact words are not important; just get the point across firmly.
- If you feel comfortable and capable, you may try to clear spirit attachments and visitations on your own. Make sure that you have adequately protected yourself before you begin, and do make sure you are in good health and properly nourished. This is important.

If you need help on getting started you can find information on spirit attachments by exploring many of the books on the subject, or on the Internet. Yes, there are numerous anecdotal methods for dealing with spirit encounters, and many do work. Just find the method that seems to fit your situation best. In many cases the key is to develop a dialogue or an understanding with the spirit and to find out why they're in your space or in your face, and what they're trying to tell you. Once you do you can use this knowledge to help them cross over to the light. Yes, clearing unwanted spirits is really quite similar to what you see on the TV show "The Ghost Whisperer."

Caution: If you're feeling uneasy or uncomfortable clearing these spirits, if you're poorly nourished or feeling weak, or if you're feeling threatened, do NOT attempt to clear these spirits on your own. Seek professional help.

Sensitive's summary:

Ultra-sensitives attract entities. These entities love our energy. Remember that spirits are like fleas. They can jump from person to person, even from great distances, and they can come from almost anybody onto you. Be prepared, and protect your sensitive self.

How to

Survive Getting Out of Bed Each Morning

This may seem like a simple task for most people. But if you are an ultra-sensitive, getting out of bed can be a daunting task, especially if you plan on landing in an upright position. Once those eyelids start fluttering, many of us wake up, look around and ask those magical questions: "Where am I?" and "Why am I here?"

Then there's the challenge of dodging those all too common bouts of light-headedness and disorientation when your logical left-brain stirs awake.

Okay, now it's safe to stumble over to the sink. That's right. Crank up the cold water; splash it on your face. Can you see your face? What color is it? If it's not Casper white, you're ready to carry on with your day and address the all-too-common ultra-sensitive dilemma: "What am I going to do today?" Not sure? That's okay. You're an ultra-sensitive. You have every right to be lost and confused from time to time.

Here's the fix:

- Eat some protein for breakfast, like a hamburger, turkey sandwich, a steak, or maybe some salmon with broccoli. If you're vegetarian eat some eggs or cheese, or just a bowl full of your favorite vegetables. Who said these things are reserved for lunch or dinner? Probably not a sensitive. Chow down. But whatever you do, don't skip breakfast, or any other meal for that matter.
- Don't even attempt to open the newspaper. Instead, use it to cover the TV screen that's broadcasting the dreadful morning news. Likely there's nothing on the tube that will help you through your day, anyway.
- Brush your teeth with that all natural toothpaste. No fluoride or artificial ingredients, please. Everything that gets into your mouth is

quickly absorbed into the blood stream, and God knows we don't need any more toxins in our bodies.

- Find something important to do today. If you don't have to work for an hourly wage, congratulations! If you do, make the most of your day, knowing that it's all just temporary. (I hate when people say it's just temporary, don't you? A lifetime is temporary, too). If your schedule is wide open, spend your day doing something creative.
- Be very excellent to yourself today, and everyday. You deserve to be pampered. After all, it takes a lot more work and energy than most people understand just to get through a day, even if you're just hanging around your home...being creative.
- Enjoy eating a fun dinner. Include plenty of complex carbohydrates, such as veggies and beans, and some protein, but nothing too heavy. Grab a nibble of your favorite sweet, if you have the urge. Even a glass of wine is nice, if you wish, or even a beer. You've earned it.
- It's evening now. Soak yourself in a salt and soda bath for twenty minutes or so. Use 1/4 cup sea salt and 1/4 cup of baking soda. This will clear away the negative energies you've picked up through the day, and trust me, you have some. (See Part I: *You Are an Empath*)
- By this time you're probably wondering when you can start looking for your bed again. Go ahead and search for it. You'll find it. After all, you are intuitive, and you are an ultra-sensitive and you need your rest. Tomorrow's a new day.

Sensitive's summary:

Getting out of bed can be hazardous to your health. Prepare yourself.

How to

Cope with a Nine-to-Five Job

There comes a time in our life as an ultra-sensitive when we have to find a way to make money in order to survive. It is the moment of reckoning, really. Although many of us pray to be given the abundance to exist in this society without having to subject ourselves to the stresses of a nine-to-five job, sometimes we just have to suck it up and work for somebody else. After all, most of us have bills to pay, at least for now.

I was the tender age of fifteen when I got my first job, serving up Big Macs and milk shakes at McDonald's. I loved the challenge of this new experience until my ultra-sensitivity caught up with me. Within six months of the intense energy exposures of this environment, I was flung into a massive funk from which it took me years to recover.

So when duty calls, how do you cope with that mandatory employment situation?

Here's the fix:

- Protect yourself. I mean this literally. Carry dark stones on your person to ward off the negativity and intense energies of your "colleagues," your electric environment, and your customers. (See Part 1: *You Are an Empath*)
- Psych yourself up each day before you get into the car or onto the bus or bike. Place a protective shield of energy around yourself to protect your aura. Develop and use regularly a mantra that works for you, asking that your high guides protect you during your excursion away from your home and sanctuary.
- Make sure you take your full allotment of breaks and your lunch while at work. You may also find it more comfortable to take these breaks alone, in the privacy and comfort of your own energy field.

You may, however, choose to connect with a particular colleague, if the connection feels nurturing and supportive. Trust your intuition.

- Take a special item with you from home that keeps you connected to your higher self and your sacred home-space. This might be a picture of a loved one or your pet or a sacred object like a stone or other spiritual item that makes you feel safe and at ease.
- Keep a bottle of inositol with you at all times. I have thousands of patients who will not leave home without it. Inositol is a B vitamin that helps quell feelings of apprehension or anxiety. It takes the edge off without making you feel groggy, and it's not habit forming. If you're headed to a meeting or other stressful situation, take 500 to 1000mg ten to fifteen minutes prior to the event. L-theanine, a derivative of green tea, may also be used to reduce stress at work and help you get through the day. Choose one or the other, but don't be afraid to give them a try. They are both safe and can help you survive, even thrive, in the harsh environment outside the front door.
- It always helps to choose an area of employment that has at least some connection to your interests. Avoid jobs that grate on your energy or work against your core belief system. If you love healing people, working in a morgue may not be suitable.
- Avoid high stress work environments and jobs where you must over-exert yourself physically or emotionally. Remember, you're not like everyone else in the workplace. You are an ultra-sensitive. So don't try to emulate or prove yourself to anyone else. Do a good job, and go home.

Sensitive's summary:

Make a diligent effort to develop home-based income-producing opportunities so you can limit your exposure to the often-insensitive work environments that await. When all else fails, make the trek to the office, but by all means protect yourself.

How to

Enjoy Sensitive Sex

Why did I decide to include this topic in the book? Because most ultra-sensitives don't want to talk about it. But we need to. That's because the physical and emotional expression of love, both in the giving and the receiving, is one of the most neglected and overlooked aspects of the ultra-sensitive's life. Yet it remains one of the most powerful healing modalities each of us has in our personal healing arsenal.

Sexual expression is not only a crucial part of our overall healing process; it is a key aspect of the expression of our sensitive selves. It's also a necessary biological function that can help us sustain our physical, emotional, spiritual, and mental vitality. In fact, sexual expression is especially crucial to the healing of the heart, not just as an emotional (energetic) healing of the heart, but a physical healing, as well.

Like other types of suppressed energies, unexpressed sexual energy and desires can lead to physical and emotional symptoms, including severe hormone imbalances, liver congestion, depression, and ultimately, *real* physical heart problems.

Here's the fix:

- Love deeply. Love often. The concept of love should not be news to the ultra-sensitive. We're all about love. Our existence is all about love. It's true that ultra-sensitives are not the only ones to have had their hearts broken. But our hearts, like our other organs, are more sensitive than others. In fact, we've had our hearts hurt and abused physically and emotionally so many times, over so many lifetimes, that many ultra-sensitives choose to do without real physical love, often without even knowing why. Hence, living without love often becomes a subconscious choice. But wait. Things are different now. Times are changing. It's time to give love another chance!

- Work hard to overcome the fear of love, the fear of being in love, the fear of commitment, and the fear of rejection. Sure it's prudent to be discerning when it comes to choosing with whom you wish to share your love. Be discerning, but not evasive. When you're ready to receive love, take down the emotional stop sign and you will attract suitable suitors.
- If you sense you are harboring the impacts of past-life sexual trauma or intense feelings of shame and guilt, or if you have experienced sexual traumas in your current life, consider a regression session to heal and reverse these issues. It's powerful medicine, and can achieve profound, immediate, and long lasting results.
- Too tired to have sex? Make sure you're eating a balanced diet that includes plenty of protein. Commence a regimen of pantothenic acid 500mg twice daily for adrenal stamina, and a B-complex 50 to 100mg daily with breakfast. Get seven to nine hours of sleep every night. If you need help achieving this, review the chapter on *How to Deal with Insomnia*.
- Balance your hormones! This is an issue for both genders, but for women, the lack of libido and interest has *everything* to do with low progesterone levels and fluctuating estrogen and testosterone levels, especially after the age of forty.
- Start using topical progesterone cream, available without a prescription from your practitioner or health food store. The typical starting dose for peri or post-menopausal women who are not cycling or cycling irregularly is ¼ to ½ teaspoonful applied topically every bedtime for first twenty-one calendar days of each month. Stay with this regimen, and watch your libido begin to come alive again. If you are having hot flashes or other hormonal symptoms, get your hormone levels checked by a qualified holistic practitioner as soon as possible
- Engage in sexual intercourse whenever and however you choose. This is a biological function that needs to be attended to. Do it regularly, and allow yourself to enjoy it without guilt or shame. No, really. It is your birthright. Just go for it. You will feel better physically, emotionally, and spiritually. Remember, once you've really let go, sexual expression can become a powerful connection to your higher

self and the higher realms. You may choose to learn more by exploring the concept of Tantric sex.
- Finally, if you make the personal choice to be celibate, honor that as well. Just find a practical way to achieve some form of sexual expression and gratification.

Sensitive's summary:

Sexual expression is healing; sexual repression can make you sick. Learn to enjoy all the physical and emotional pleasure that sharing your love can bring, and you will be healthier for it.

How to

Avoid Suicide

Now, this may sound like a presumptuous and even morbid topic. But let's be serious for a moment. Living the life of an ultra-sensitive is not easy. You know that. That's why you're reading this book--to learn how to make your life more tolerable, even fulfilling. And let's be clear. Living a joyful and fulfilling life is not only possible, it's also your birthright.

Yet, our lives are often filled with an over-abundance of disappointment, obstacles, difficult relationships and people, and failures. These add up. They take a toll on the spirit and life energy of the ultra-sensitive, often making us feel like the whole life process is futile. Many of the ultra-sensitives I work with report they often have suicidal thoughts. They want to give up and go home. But not yet, please. You've got important things to do.

DON'T GIVE UP NOW! You are so close to that pot of gold you've been sensing and hearing about. Remember this. You came down here to do something important during these unparalleled and historic times. There's never been a time like this on this planet before. You chose to be here to experience it all. So be here!

Here's the fix:

- Become more social. Get out there and mingle with people of your own like and kind. Unfortunately, ultra-sensitives tend to cloister themselves *away* from society, often becoming hermits because of their inability to tolerate the harsh energies out there. But over time, being isolated can lead to depression, anxiety, and other illnesses. Find spiritual support groups, spiritual events and classes. Go there. Get involved with like-minded people NOW! This is the time.

- Cry! But cry with a purpose. Crying is the most powerful healing and cleansing technique around. When you feel like crying, tune into to exactly what feelings and emotions you are experiencing. Pay close attention to what's bothering you, what's really behind each emotion. Then take steps to resolve each of the conflicts that are bringing on the emotion. You CAN do this. Whatever these issues are, acknowledge them, honor them, and then release them, for good, because it's time to move on. If you need help with this contact my office.
- Get a mate. Having a mate by your side through these thin times can make life not only exponentially better and more tolerable, but much more pleasurable. We deserve this. Surviving with a partner is always easier. Many of us lack the drive and motivation to find a mate. We've been hurt in so many relationships before we don't even want to try. Step out of the pity past. Maybe you believe you've got so much baggage that no one will ever want you. You may even think you are damaged goods. Not true. Your potential mate probably feels exactly the same way. This is now. If you really want a mate, get a mate. There is one waiting for you if you'll just allow yourself to open to it. Remember your auric field? People feel your "stop sign," your energy imprint that sends out the message that you're not available, even if you are. Turn off the stop sign. If you haven't felt it yet, now is the time for the "green light." So get going.
- Get a hobby. There are things that you loved to do during your childhood and teen years that likely still interest you today. Find them. Rediscover them. Did you love to write, sing, dance, build toy cars… teach others? Find your fire. Find your joy. Find your passion. It's in there, I promise. Think back on what you used to love to do and start doing these things again. Your passion for living will re-ignite.
- Get a regression session from a qualified practitioner. Past life traumas are often at the root cause of longstanding feelings of sadness and hopelessness, and more. These traumas and their emotional stronghold over you can be effectively cleared and neutralized with a properly performed regression session.
- Connect with yourself and the higher realms. Meditate on a regular basis to find your long lost inspiration. You came here for a purpose. When you find out what that is, your life will most certainly become

worth living, and worth living to the fullest. (See Part 1: *Why Am I Here, Really?)*

Feeling lost, hopeless, and confused is often an unfortunate part of the journey for many ultra-sensitives, but it certainly doesn't have to control your fate. Your life is valuable. Take whatever steps are necessary to bring back your zest for living. That may mean making wholesale changes in your living arrangements, job situation, and even relationships. Don't be afraid to make those changes. If you reach a point where you need professional assistance, reach out for it. It's available. But don't you go anywhere. You are needed by so many, many of whom you don't even yet know.

Sensitive's summary:

Living the life of an ultra-sensitive can be a challenging experience fraught with extreme pitfalls and disappointments and complicated by people who just don't get you. It's no wonder so many have questioned their willingness to continue on this path. Yet, understanding who you really are and what you really came here to do can bring you the fortitude, the courage, and the inspiration to carry on.

How to

Communicate with Your Guides

This is a topic covered by hundreds, if not thousands, of authors in various formats. Here are some new thoughts on the subject, relative to those who are ultra-sensitive. In other words, *you!*

First, your guides can be anyone--a passed over loved one or one of your many high guides or angels. If you can determine a name or an identity of your guide, that's great. If not, that's okay too.

Communicating with your guides does not necessarily have to be a woo-woo, complicated, mysterious thing that takes place between gurus and the highest of the high. It happens all day, every day in the subtlest circumstances, even when you don't realize it. How can you open the channels of communication with your guides?

Here's the fix:

- Start paying attention to the voice in your head. You may think that's you in there, and sometimes it is. Sometimes it isn't. Sometimes it's someone who cares about you, who's watching over you. It may not be the Source or the highest of the highest, but it may still be a source of information that is important or relevant to a current situation, or even to your overall life path. Be discerning. If your intuition tells you the information is valid, trust what you get, whether it's your voice or another. On the other hand, if what you're feeling or hearing doesn't feel right, get rid of it.
- ***Note of caution*:** There can be times and circumstances when negative spirit entities or energies may be trying to communicate with you or influence you in a negative way. If what you're receiving feels completely wrong or makes you feel apprehensive or worse, be

cautious. If this type of communication persists, obtain an entity clearing from a qualified energy practitioner, or reach my office.

- Pay attention to your dreams. Pay attention to the themes of your dreams. There's a message in there and it's for you. Keep a good dream journal, and then start putting the puzzle pieces together. When you look closely enough at what you've been dreaming about you may discover an important message. Trust what you get. Explore these dream images and themes further in one of the many dream interpretation books available.
- Meditate daily. Now for some, this notion is a turn-off. So let's make it simple. For the ultra-sensitive, meditation and the insights that it brings can happen anytime during your waking hours, even when you are doing just about anything else. Many ultra-sensitives, including this author, receive messages during the day while showering or bathing (water is a great spirit conductor), driving a car, writing a book or other material, gazing at the stars, or any other event that keeps you out of your left logical brain.
- Sit quietly, writing paper ready and pen in hand, and be patient. It may take several attempts, even over weeks or months, but chances are someone, somewhere is going to channel to you and through you, perhaps one of your guides or a passed-over loved one. Story has it that Neale Donald Walsch was quite successful using this method.
- Pay close attention to the subtle signs that are being presented to you during your waking hours. You may find the answers you're searching for on a billboard or a bumper sticker, or in the lyrics of a song. Not all guidance comes with fanfare or an affidavit. Just be patient, open, and ready to receive.
- Keep your chakras clear and balanced at all times, especially your crown and third-eye charkas. These are the key chakras that seem to be most receptive to energy and sprit influence. Work with your holistic practitioner, or begin to develop these chakra clearing and balancing skills on your own.

As an ultra-sensitive, you are receiving spirit input 24/7, even and especially when you don't realize it. If this input begins to overwhelm you or keep you awake, or you need it to cease for any reason, be direct and firm with the sender. Tell them to leave you alone for the night, or any other period of time that you need to rest. Remember, you do have control over the frequency and the volume of the input you wish to receive. Exercise it. On the other side of the coin, don't hesitate to thank your spirit guides for the insight they bring you whenever it is appropriate. Grateful is good.

Sensitive's summary:

One of our jobs as ultra-sensitives is to receive information and disseminate it to those who are ready to do something important with it. Carry on. This book is a shining example of that process.

How to

Experience Joy in Your Life

Are you experiencing all the joy in your life that you're truly capable of experiencing? Do you sometimes feel like there's got to be something more, that there's something missing? Yes, we all feel that way from time to time, but for many ultra-sensitives this feeling of incompletion seems to be an all-too-common event.

What's more, some ultra-sensitives seem to feel that no matter how much they achieve or accomplish in their lives, it's not enough. It's *never* enough. They just keep raising the bar higher and higher, reaching for the next rung on the ladder to the elusive "success." So, when you're that busy constantly trying to achieve, how do you find time to experience real joy in your life?

It took some authentic soul searching, but after much contemplation I have collected a string of pearls to help resolve this dilemma, for the ultra-sensitives and the less-sensitives alike.

Here's the fix:

- Don't save anything for a rainy day, because it can rain at any moment. Remember, you're not taking any of these material things with you when you transition to your next assignment. So enjoy everything now.
- Don't live for tomorrow. Enjoy all you can in the now. It's all you really have: the right now. Find the joy in every moment, no matter how mundane that moment may seem. Every moment is a gift, no matter how painful or difficult it may seem at the time.
- Set realistic expectations for success and joy. Joy doesn't always come with a fanfare, and it doesn't always come knocking at your door, but it does need an invitation. So ask for it by name.

- Don't compare yourself with others. What brings others joy may not bring you joy, and vice versa. Besides, you don't know what's really going on behind their closed doors.
- Slow down and set life priorities. Get rid of your self-induced "honey do" list. Choose your lessons thoughtfully so that you're not doing things you really don't want to do.
- Banish all negativity from your life: negative people, negative relationships, negative routines, negative thoughts, negative situations. If it doesn't bring you joy, cut it loose.
- Don't let the unhappiness of others bring you down. Or, said differently, don't try to learn the lessons of others. Don't take on their baggage. That's theirs. The sooner you delegate lessons back to their rightful owners, the sooner you'll find joy in your life.
- Pay heed to one of my first and oldest theorems: **Expectations lead to disappointment**. Instead of expecting, *intend,* then you won't be disappointed. But do also understand that the universe will give you what you need, regardless.
- Don't look to the outer world for joy. It's waiting for you on the inside. For many ultra-sensitives, joy may simply be finding peace of mind or getting through the day. Enjoy that.
- Find yourself in nature. That is, find out who you are through your experiences with nature. Nature is the essential building block of authentic joy. It's where it all starts. It's where *we* started. You can experience nature in your own backyard, on your small patio, or through a telescope. Just get back to the essence of nature.
- Don't rely on others to bring you joy. True joy is something only you can bring to yourself.
- Understand that this journey we call life is not your first journey, and for most, not your last. That will relieve some of the pressure of trying to do everything and be everything this time around, and allow you more time to experience more joy, now.

Sensitive's summary:

For many ultra-sensitives, there is a fine line between what we perceive as joy and what we perceive as work. If you look at your

life from a higher perspective you will notice that you can find the joy in everyone and everything. So *that's* where it's been hiding!

About the Author

Dr. Emil Faithe is a Medical Intuitive and Metaphysician, and the co-founder of World Wellness Center in Albuquerque, New Mexico. He works with all conditions and all ages, across the globe. More information is available at his website: **www.truenw.com**.

CPSIA information can be obtained
at www.ICGtesting.com
Printed in the USA
FSOW01n0441080415
6219FS